The Open University

M208 Pure

AB3

Integration

This publication forms part of an Open University course. Details of this and other Open University courses can be obtained from the Student Registration and Enquiry Service, The Open University, PO Box 197, Milton Keynes, MK7 6BJ, United Kingdom: tel. +44 (0)870 333 4340, e-mail general-enquiries@open.ac.uk

Alternatively, you may visit the Open University website at http://www.open.ac.uk where you can learn more about the wide range of courses and packs offered at all levels by The Open University.

To purchase a selection of Open University course materials, visit the webshop at www.ouw.co.uk, or contact Open University Worldwide, Michael Young Building, Walton Hall, Milton Keynes, MK7 6AA, United Kingdom, for a brochure: tel. +44 (0)1908 858785, fax +44 (0)1908 858787, e-mail ouwenq@open.ac.uk

The Open University, Walton Hall, Milton Keynes, MK7 6AA.

First published 2006.

Edited, designed and typeset by The Open University, using the Open University TeX System.

Printed and bound in the United Kingdom by Hobbs the Printers Limited, Brunel Road, Totton, Hampshire SO40 3WX.

ISBN 0 7492 0213 0

1.1

Contents

Introduction

In Analysis Block A we used the idea of the *area* enclosed by a circle to define the number π. This method showed that the area of even such a simple set needs careful definition. In this unit we consider the question:

See Unit AA2, Subsection 5.2.

what do we mean by the area between a graph and the x-axis?

We answer this question in Section 1 by introducing a process of trapping the required area between increasingly accurate lower and upper estimates, each of which is the sum of the areas of suitably chosen rectangles.

Usually accurate upper and lower estimates are obtained by using many rectangles whose widths are small.

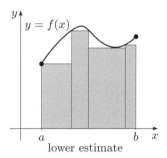
lower estimate

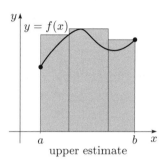
upper estimate

The area between the graph $y = f(x)$ and the segment $[a, b]$ of the x-axis is defined to be the supremum of the lower estimates and the infimum of the upper estimates, as long as these two values are equal. In this case, we call the common value the *integral* of f on $[a, b]$, written

$$\int_a^b f \quad \text{or} \quad \int_a^b f(x)\, dx.$$

For many functions f, we can evaluate integrals by using the *Fundamental Theorem of Calculus*, which asserts that

$$\int_a^b f = F(b) - F(a),$$

where F is any function, called a *primitive* of F, such that

$$F'(x) = f(x), \quad \text{for } x \in [a, b].$$

It follows from the Fundamental Theorem of Calculus that we can think of integration as the inverse operation of differentiation.

In Section 2 we use rules arising from this theorem to evaluate many integrals explicitly.

Often, however, it is not possible to evaluate an integral explicitly, and the best we can do is to obtain upper and lower bounds for its value. In Section 3 we establish some inequalities for integrals, such as the Triangle Inequality,

$$\left| \int_a^b f \right| \le \int_a^b |f|.$$

We also use these inequalities for integrals to prove Wallis' Formula,

$$\lim_{n \to \infty} \frac{(n!)^2 2^{2n}}{(2n)! \sqrt{n}} = \sqrt{\pi},$$

and to establish the Integral Test, which enables us to determine the behaviour of series such as $\sum 1/n^p$, where $p > 0$, and $\sum 1/(n \log_e n)$.

In Section 4 we discuss the value of the quantity $n!$, which arises in many problems in probability. Integration techniques give an excellent estimate for $n!$, called Stirling's Formula, which can be expressed as

$$\lim_{n \to \infty} \frac{n!}{\sqrt{2\pi n}\,(n/e)^n} = 1.$$

Study guide

The sections should be read in their natural order. Section 1 includes the audio section and Section 4 includes the video section. Subsection 1.3 is optional; it contains a number of proofs, some quite complicated, of results given in the audio section. A large part of Section 2 is revision of material covered in earlier courses.

You should have your calculator handy while you work through this unit.

1   Riemann integral

After working through this section, you should be able to:

(a) determine the *lower Riemann sum* $L(f, P)$ and the *upper Riemann sum* $U(f, P)$ for a given function f and *partition* P;

(b) understand the definition of the *integral* $\int_a^b f$;

(c) use upper and lower sums to determine whether a given function is *integrable*;

(d) use basic rules for manipulating integrals;

(e) state various sufficient conditions for a function to be integrable.

1.1 What is area?

In the audio section we give a rigorous definition of what we mean by the area between the graph

$$y = f(x) \quad (x \in [a, b])$$

and the interval $[a, b]$ on the x-axis. We want such a definition to agree with our intuitive notion of area.

However, it is not obvious that we can always say that the region between a graph and the x-axis *has* an area. For example, can we define such an area for the following functions?

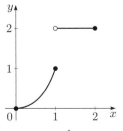

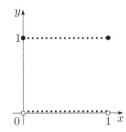

(a) $f(x) = \begin{cases} x^2, & 0 \le x \le 1, \\ 2, & 1 < x \le 2. \end{cases}$

(b) $f(x) = \begin{cases} 1, & 0 \le x \le 1, \quad x \text{ rational}, \\ 0, & 0 \le x \le 1, \quad x \text{ irrational}. \end{cases}$

5

Our approach is to find lower and upper estimates for the area (if it exists) of the region between the graph and the x-axis. Each estimate is the area of a union of rectangles.

First we divide the interval $[a, b]$ into a set of subintervals, called a *partition* of $[a, b]$. Then we consider two sets of rectangles, each rectangle having one of the subintervals as its base. In one set, we choose rectangles whose top edges lie on or below the graph, so the sum of their individual areas forms a lower estimate for the 'area' of the region; in the other, we choose rectangles whose top edges lie on or above the graph, so the sum of their individual areas forms an upper estimate for the 'area'.

In Unit AA1, Section 5, we used approximating triangles rather than rectangles to define π as the area of a circle of radius 1.

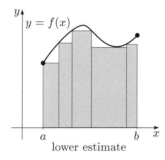
lower estimate

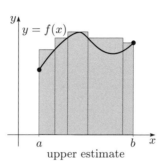
upper estimate

In this way we can obtain many lower estimates and upper estimates, by choosing different partitions of $[a, b]$. If there is a real number A with the properties

the supremum of the lower estimates $= A$

and

the infimum of the upper estimates $= A$,

then we define A to be the *area* between the graph and the x-axis.

We find that we can define such an area for graph (a) on page 5, but not for graph (b).

1.2 Definition of the integral

In this audio section we define the *integral* of a bounded function f on an interval $[a, b]$. This is a formalisation, due to Riemann, of the method outlined in Subsection 1.1 for defining the area between the graph

The integral we define is often called the *Riemann integral*.

$$y = f(x) \quad (x \in [a, b]),$$

and the segment $[a, b]$ of the x-axis.

In the audio we use the shorthand notations

$$\min f = \min\{f(x) : a \le x \le b\}, \quad \max f = \max\{f(x) : a \le x \le b\},$$

whenever these quantities are defined, and

$$\inf f = \inf\{f(x) : a \le x \le b\}, \quad \sup f = \sup\{f(x) : a \le x \le b\}.$$

See Unit AA1, Section 4, for the definitions of sup and inf.

To make clear which interval is involved, we write $\min_{[a,b]} f$, and so on.

Also, we use the following identities:

See Unit I2, Exercises 3.7 and 3.19.

$$1 + 2 + 3 + \cdots + n = \sum_{i=1}^{n} i = \tfrac{1}{2}n(n+1),$$

$$1^2 + 2^2 + 3^2 + \cdots + n^2 = \sum_{i=1}^{n} i^2 = \tfrac{1}{6}n(n+1)(2n+1).$$

Listen to the audio as you work through the frames.

Audio

1. Minimum and maximum

$$\min f = m \text{ if :}$$

1. $f(x) \geq m$,   all $x \in [a, b]$
2. $f(c) = m$,   some $c \in [a, b]$.

$$\max f = M \text{ if :}$$

1. $f(x) \leq M$,   all $x \in [a, b]$
2. $f(d) = M$,   some $d \in [a, b]$.

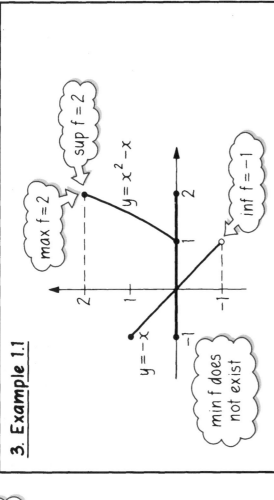

exist if f continuous on $[a,b]$

$y = f(x)$

2. Infimum and supremum

$$\inf f = m \text{ if}$$

1. $f(x) \geq m$,   all $x \in [a, b]$
2. $m' > m$
   $\Rightarrow f(c) < m'$, some $c \in [a, b]$.

$$\sup f = M \text{ if}$$

1. $f(x) \leq M$,   all $x \in [a, b]$
2. $M' < M$
   $\Rightarrow f(d) > M'$, some $d \in [a, b]$.

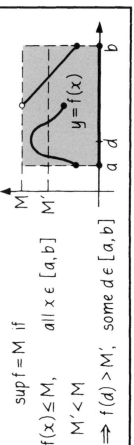
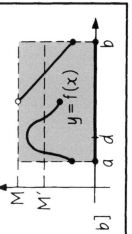

exist if f bounded on $[a,b]$

$y = f(x)$

3. Example 1.1

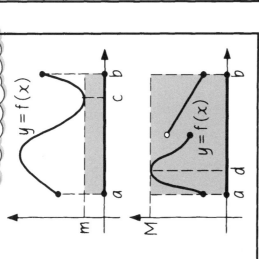
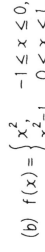

$\sup f = 2$

$\max f = 2$

$y = x^2 - x$

$\inf f = -1$

$y = -x$

min f does not exist

4. Exercise 1.1

For each of the functions f on $[-1, 1]$,

identify the following (if they exist) :

$$\min f, \quad \max f, \quad \inf f, \quad \sup f.$$

(a) $f(x) = \begin{cases} x^2, & -1 < x < 1, \\ \frac{1}{2}, & x = \pm 1; \end{cases}$

(b) $f(x) = \begin{cases} x^2, & -1 \leq x \leq 0, \\ x^2 - 1, & 0 < x \leq 1. \end{cases}$

Sketch the graph first

5. Partitions of $[a,b]$

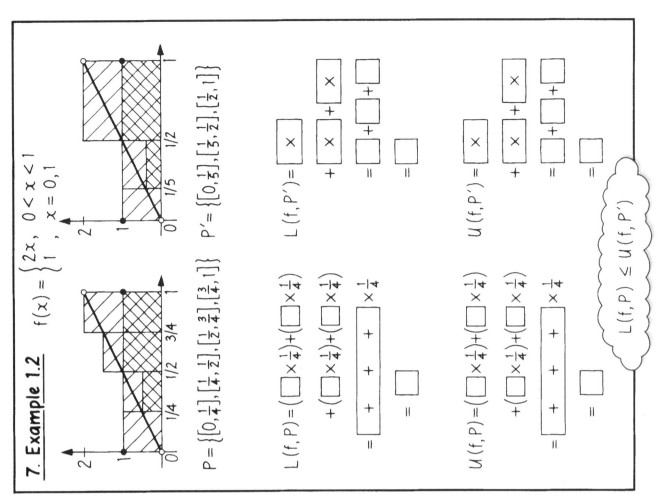

$m_i = \inf\limits_{[x_{i-1}, x_i]} f$

$M_i = \sup\limits_{[x_{i-1}, x_i]} f$

$y = f(x)$

$a = x_0 \;\; x_1 \;\; x_2 \ldots \;\; x_{i-1} \;\; x_i \, x_{n-1} \;\; x_n = b \quad \delta x_i = x_i - x_{i-1}$

$\leftarrow \delta x_i \rightarrow$

$P = \{[x_0, x_1], [x_1, x_2]\ldots, [x_{i-1}, x_i],\ldots, [x_{n-1}, x_n]\}$

Mesh of P: $\|P\| = \max\limits_{1 \le i \le n} \delta x_i$

standard partition has equal subintervals

6. Lower and upper Riemann sums

$y = f(x)$

Lower sum

$x_0 \; x_1 \quad x_2 \quad x_3$

$m_1, \; m_2, \; m_3$

Upper sum

$M_1, \; M_2, \; M_3$

$x_0 \; x_1 \quad x_2 \quad x_3$

$L(f,P) = \sum\limits_{i=1}^{n} m_i\, \delta x_i \;\; \le \;\; \sum\limits_{i=1}^{n} M_i\, \delta x_i = U(f,P)$

7. Example 1.2

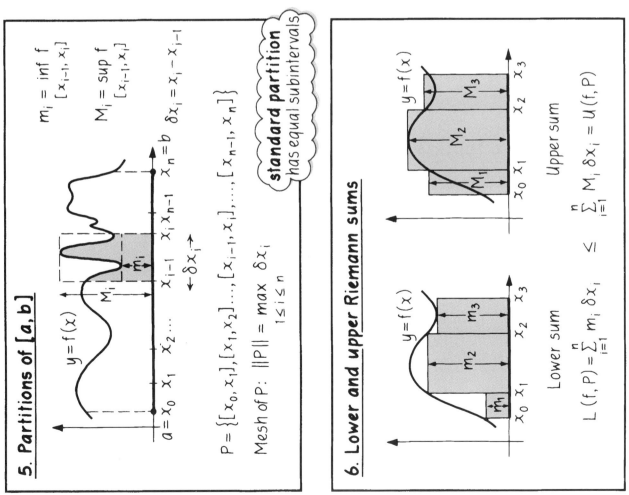

$$f(x) = \begin{cases} 2x, & 0 < x < 1 \\ 1, & x = 0, 1 \end{cases}$$

$P = \left\{[0, \tfrac{1}{4}], [\tfrac{1}{4}, \tfrac{1}{2}], [\tfrac{1}{2}, \tfrac{3}{4}], [\tfrac{3}{4}, 1]\right\}$

$L(f,P) = (\square \times \tfrac{1}{4}) + (\square \times \tfrac{1}{4}) + (\square \times \tfrac{1}{4}) + (\square \times \tfrac{1}{4})$
$= \square + \square + \square + \square = \square$

$U(f,P) = (\square \times \tfrac{1}{4}) + (\square \times \tfrac{1}{4}) + (\square \times \tfrac{1}{4}) + (\square \times \tfrac{1}{4})$
$= \square + \square + \square + \square = \square$

$P' = \left\{[0, \tfrac{1}{5}], [\tfrac{1}{5}, \tfrac{1}{2}], [\tfrac{1}{2}, 1]\right\}$

$L(f,P') = \square + \square + \square = \square$

$U(f,P') = \square + \square + \square = \square$

$L(f,P) \le U(f,P')$

8. Example 1.3

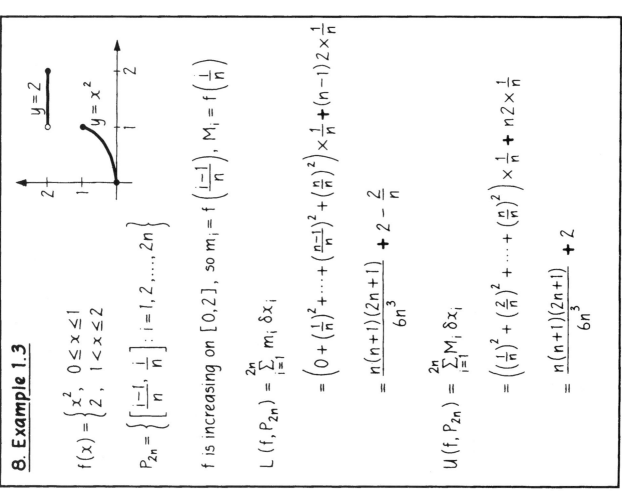

$$f(x) = \begin{cases} x^2, & 0 \le x \le 1 \\ 2, & 1 < x \le 2 \end{cases}$$

$$P_{2n} = \left\{ \left[\frac{i-1}{n}, \frac{i}{n} \right] : i = 1, 2, \ldots, 2n \right\}$$

f is increasing on $[0,2]$, so $m_i = f\left(\frac{i-1}{n}\right)$, $M_i = f\left(\frac{i}{n}\right)$

$$L(f, P_{2n}) = \sum_{i=1}^{2n} m_i\, \delta x_i$$

$$= \left(0 + \left(\frac{1}{n}\right)^2 + \cdots + \left(\frac{n-1}{n}\right)^2 + \left(\frac{n}{n}\right)^2 \right) \times \frac{1}{n} + (n-1)2 \times \frac{1}{n}$$

$$= \frac{n(n+1)(2n+1)}{6n^3} + 2 - \frac{2}{n}$$

$$U(f, P_{2n}) = \sum_{i=1}^{2n} M_i\, \delta x_i$$

$$= \left(\left(\frac{1}{n}\right)^2 + \left(\frac{2}{n}\right)^2 + \cdots + \left(\frac{n}{n}\right)^2 \right) \times \frac{1}{n} + n2 \times \frac{1}{n}$$

$$= \frac{n(n+1)(2n+1)}{6n^3} + 2$$

9. Example 1.3 continued

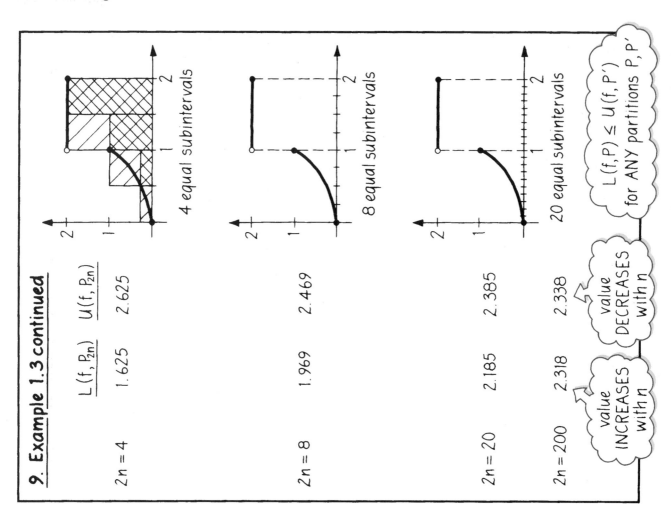

	$L(f, P_{2n})$	$U(f, P_{2n})$
$2n = 4$	1.625	2.625
$2n = 8$	1.969	2.469
$2n = 20$	2.185	2.385
$2n = 200$	2.318	2.338

4 equal subintervals

8 equal subintervals

20 equal subintervals

value INCREASES with n

value DECREASES with n

$L(f, P) \le U(f, P')$ for ANY partitions P, P'

12. Example 1.3 continued

$$L(f, P_{2n}) = \frac{n(n+1)(2n+1)}{6n^3} + 2 - \frac{2}{n} = \frac{1}{6}\left(1+\frac{1}{n}\right)\left(2+\frac{1}{n}\right) + 2 - \frac{2}{n}$$

$$U(f, P_{2n}) = \frac{n(n+1)(2n+1)}{6n^3} + 2 = \frac{1}{6}\left(1+\frac{1}{n}\right)\left(2+\frac{1}{n}\right) + 2$$

$$\lim_{n \to \infty} L(f, P_{2n}) = \boxed{} \quad ; \quad \lim_{n \to \infty} U(f, P_{2n}) = \boxed{}$$

$$\text{Hence} \quad \underline{\int_0^2} f \geq \boxed{} \quad \text{and} \quad \overline{\int_0^2} f \leq \boxed{}$$

$$\text{So,} \quad \boxed{} \leq \underline{\int_0^2} f \leq \overline{\int_0^2} f \leq \boxed{}$$

$$\text{It follows that} \quad \underline{\int_0^2} f = \overline{\int_0^2} f = \boxed{}$$

13. Dirichlet's function

$$f(x) = \begin{cases} 1, & 0 \leq x \leq 1, \ x \text{ rational} \\ 0, & 0 \leq x \leq 1, \ x \text{ irrational} \end{cases}$$

$$L(f, P) = \sum_{i=1}^{n} m_i \, \delta x_i = \sum_{i=1}^{n} 0 \times \delta x_i = 0$$

$$U(f, P) = \sum_{i=1}^{n} M_i \, \delta x_i = \sum_{i=1}^{n} 1 \times \delta x_i = 1$$

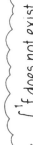

$\int_0^1 f$ does not exist

10. An important inequality

Theorem 1.1

For ANY partitions P, P' of $[a, b]$,

$$L(f, P) \leq U(f, P').$$

$\{L(f, P)\}$ is bounded above
$\{U(f, P)\}$ is bounded below

11. Definitions

- **Lower integral**

$$\underline{\int_a^b} f = \sup_P \left\{ L(f, P) \right\}$$

- **Upper integral**

$$\overline{\int_a^b} f = \inf_P \left\{ U(f, P) \right\}$$

$$\underline{\int} f \leq \overline{\int} f$$

- f is **integrable** on $[a, b]$

$$\iff \underline{\int_a^b} f \text{ and } \overline{\int_a^b} f \text{ exist}$$

$$\text{AND}$$

$$\underline{\int_a^b} f = \overline{\int_a^b} f = \int_a^b f$$

f bounded on $[a, b]$
$\implies \underline{\int} f, \overline{\int} f$ exist
BUT may have different values

- $\int_a^b f$ is the **integral** of f on $[a, b]$

16. Is *bounded* f *integrable on* [a,b]?

Strategy 1.1 For determining integrability

1. choose ANY sequence of partitions $\{P_n\}$, with $\|P_n\| \to 0$;

   (*often P_n is standard partition*)

2. find $L = \lim\limits_{n\to\infty} L(f,P_n)$ and $U = \lim\limits_{n\to\infty} U(f,P_n)$;

   (*Theorem 1.2*) (*Theorem 1.3*)

   • $L \neq U \implies$ f is not integrable

   • $L = U \implies$ f is integrable and $\int_a^b f = L = U$.

17. Exercise 1.2

For each of the following functions f,

determine whether f is integrable on $[0,1]$;

if it is, find $\int_0^1 f$:

(a) $f(x) = \begin{cases} -2, & 0 \leq x < 1, \\ 3, & x = 1 ; \end{cases}$

(b) $f(x) = \begin{cases} x, & 0 \leq x \leq 1, \ x \text{ rational}, \\ 0, & 0 \leq x \leq 1, \ x \text{ irrational}. \end{cases}$

14. Theorem 1.2

If f is integrable on $[a,b]$ and $\{P_n\}$

is ANY sequence of partitions of $[a,b]$,

with $\|P_n\| \to 0$, then

$$\lim_{n\to\infty} L(f,P_n) = \lim_{n\to\infty} U(f,P_n). \qquad (\ast)$$

(*$= \int_a^b f$*)

ONE sequence $\{P_n\}$ for which $(\ast)$ FAILS $\Longrightarrow$ f not integrable

15. Theorem 1.3

If there is ONE sequence $\{P_n\}$ of

partitions of $[a,b]$, with $\|P_n\| \to 0$,

for which

$$\lim_{n\to\infty} L(f,P_n) = \lim_{n\to\infty} U(f,P_n) \qquad (\ast)$$

(*$= I$*)

then

f is integrable on $[a,b]$ and $\int_a^b f = I$.

ONE sequence $\{P_n\}$ for which $(\ast)$ HOLDS $\Longrightarrow$ f integrable

18. Limits of integration

We define

- $\int_a^a f = 0$

- if $a > b$ and $\int_b^a f$ exists, then $\int_a^b f = -\int_b^a f$

19. Additivity of integrals

- $\int_a^c f$ and $\int_c^b f$ exist

  $\Rightarrow \int_a^b f$ exists   and $\int_a^b f = \int_a^c f + \int_c^b f$

- f integrable on an interval I

  $\Rightarrow$ f integrable on any subinterval of I, and

  $\int_a^b f = \int_a^c f + \int_c^b f$, for any $a, b, c \in I$

20. Sign of $\int_a^b f$

$f(x) \geq 0 \Rightarrow \int_a^b f \geq 0$ $f(x) \leq 0 \Rightarrow \int_a^b f \leq 0$

$b > a$

21. Modulus Rule

$\int_a^b f$ exists $\Rightarrow$ $\int_a^b |f|$ exists

$\int_a^b f \leq \int_a^b |f|$

22. Combination Rules

If f and g are integrable on $[a, b]$, then so are:

the **sum** $f + g$ and $\int_a^b (f + g) = \int_a^b f + \int_a^b g$

the **multiple** λf, $\lambda \in \mathbb{R}$, and $\int_a^b \lambda f = \lambda \cdot \int_a^b f$

the **product** fg

the **quotient** f/g, provided 1/g bounded on $[a, b]$.

23. Standard integrable functions

The following functions are integrable:

- continuous functions
- monotonic functions

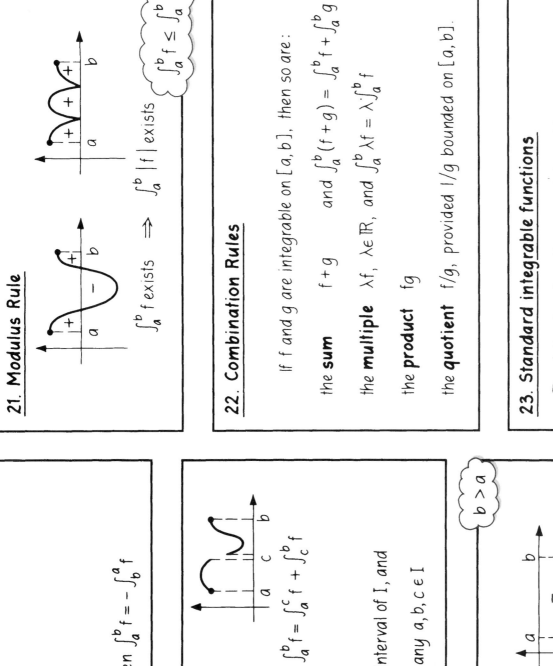

1.3 Proofs (optional)

Here we give outline proofs of several of the results in Subsection 1.2.

First recall that if f is a bounded function defined on $[a,b]$ and

$$P = \{[x_0, x_1], [x_1, x_2], \ldots, [x_{n-1}, x_n]\},$$

is a *partition* of $[a,b]$, then, for $i = 1, 2, \ldots, n$, we set

$$m_i = \inf\{f(x) : x_{i-1} \le x \le x_i\}, \quad M_i = \sup\{f(x) : x_{i-1} \le x \le x_i\}.$$

The *lower* and *upper Riemann sums* of f corresponding to P are

$$L(f, P) = \sum_{i=1}^{n} m_i \, \delta x_i \quad \text{and} \quad U(f, P) = \sum_{i=1}^{n} M_i \, \delta x_i,$$

where $\delta x_i = x_i - x_{i-1}$. The *lower* and *upper integrals* of f over $[a,b]$ are

$$\underline{\int_a^b} f = \sup_P\{L(f, P)\} \quad \text{and} \quad \overline{\int_a^b} f = \inf_P\{U(f, P)\},$$

and we say that f is *integrable* on $[a,b]$ if these lower and upper integrals are equal. The *integral* $\int_a^b f$ is then defined to be the common value of the lower and upper integrals of f over $[a,b]$.

See Frames 5, 6 and 11.

Here a and b are called limits of integration.

Criteria for integrability

In the proofs of Theorems 1.1 and 1.2, we assume that f is bounded and *non-negative* on $[a,b]$. The general versions of these theorems can be deduced by applying their 'non-negative' versions to the function $g = f + c$, where c is a constant so large that g is non-negative on $[a,b]$.

The assumption that f is non-negative simplifies some details of the proofs.

Theorem 1.1 If f is a bounded function on $[a,b]$, and both P and P' are partitions of $[a,b]$, then

$$L(f, P) \le U(f, P').$$

See Frame 10.

Proof   First we observe that for any partition P of $[a,b]$ we have

$$L(f, P) \le U(f, P).$$

This follows immediately from the definitions of $L(f, P)$ and $U(f, P)$.

We prove Theorem 1.1 by showing that if P'' is the partition of $[a,b]$ obtained by using all the partition points from both P and P', then

$$L(f, P) \le L(f, P'') \le U(f, P'') \le U(f, P'). \tag{1.1}$$

We claim that adding a new partition point x' to a partition

$$P = \{[x_0, x_1], [x_1, x_2], \ldots, [x_{n-1}, x_n]\}$$

does not increase the upper Riemann sum $U(f, P)$ and may decrease it. This is because the new point x' lies in a subinterval $[x_{i-1}, x_i]$, for some i, and the only effect on the upper Riemann sum of adding x' is to replace the rectangle with side M_i standing on $[x_{i-1}, x_i]$ with a pair of adjacent rectangles standing on $[x_{i-1}, x_i]$ with heights at most M_i, as illustrated.

Hence, adding a finite number of new partition points to P does not increase the upper Riemann sum. Similarly, adding a finite number of new partition points to P does not decrease the lower Riemann sum.

Now the partition P'' can be formed from either P or P' by adding a finite number of partition points, so inequalities (1.1) follow. ∎

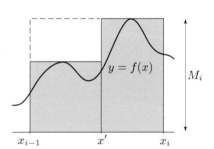

Here we use the fact that f is assumed to be non-negative on $[a,b]$.

If P is a partition of $[a, b]$, then any partition obtained from P by adding a finite number of points is called a **refinement** of P. The partition obtained from two partitions P and P' by using all their partition points is called the **common refinement** of P and P'.

Theorem 1.2   If f is an integrable function on $[a, b]$ and $\{P_n\}$ is a sequence of partitions of $[a, b]$ such that $\|P_n\| \to 0$, then

$$\lim_{n \to \infty} L(f, P_n) = \lim_{n \to \infty} U(f, P_n) = \int_a^b f.$$

See Frame 14.

Recall (from Frame 5) that $\|P_n\|$, the *mesh* of P_n, is the length of the longest subinterval of P_n.

Proof   We prove that $\lim_{n \to \infty} U(f, P_n) = \int_a^b f$.

There is a similar proof that

$$\lim_{n \to \infty} L(f, P_n) = \int_a^b f.$$

We assume that f is non-negative on $[a, b]$, so, for some $M \in \mathbb{R}$, we have

$$0 \leq f(x) \leq M, \quad \text{for } a \leq x \leq b. \tag{1.2}$$

Let $\varepsilon > 0$. Since f is integrable on $[a, b]$, there is a partition

$$P' = \{[x_0', x_1'], [x_1', x_2'], \ldots, [x_{m-1}', x_m']\}$$

of $[a, b]$, with m subintervals, such that

$$U(f, P') < \int_a^b f + \tfrac{1}{2}\varepsilon. \tag{1.3}$$

We use $\tfrac{1}{2}\varepsilon$ here in order to obtain ε later in the proof.

Now consider any partition in the sequence $\{P_n\}$, of the form

$$P_n = \{[x_0, x_1], [x_1, x_2], \ldots, [x_{p-1}, x_p]\},$$

where p is the number of subintervals in P_n. For $k = 1, 2, \ldots, p$, define

$$M_k = \sup\{f(x) : x_{k-1} \leq x \leq x_k\} \quad \text{and} \quad \delta x_k = x_k - x_{k-1}.$$

Let P_n' denote the common refinement of P' and P_n. Then, as in the proof of Theorem 1.1, we have

$$U(f, P_n') \leq U(f, P'). \tag{1.4}$$

Now we can obtain P_n from P_n' by removing at most $m - 1$ of the partition points of P'. Removing such a point x_i', lying in (x_{k-1}, x_k) say, we increase the upper Riemann sum by at most $M_k(x_k - x_{k-1})$, as illustrated. So, since $M_k \leq M$, by inequality (1.2), and $x_k - x_{k-1} \leq \|P_n\|$, for $k = 1, 2, \ldots, p$,

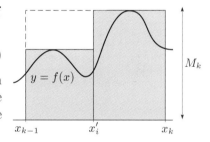

$$U(f, P_n) \leq U(f, P_n') + (m - 1)M\|P_n\|. \tag{1.5}$$

Combining inequalities (1.3), (1.4) and (1.5), we obtain

$$U(f, P_n) < \left(\int_a^b f + \tfrac{1}{2}\varepsilon \right) + (m - 1)M\|P_n\|.$$

Since $\|P_n\| \to 0$ as $n \to \infty$, we can choose N so large that

$$(m - 1)M\|P_n\| < \tfrac{1}{2}\varepsilon, \quad \text{for all } n > N,$$

We use $\tfrac{1}{2}\varepsilon$ here in order to obtain ε later in the proof.

and hence

$$U(f, P_n) < \left(\int_a^b f + \tfrac{1}{2}\varepsilon \right) + \tfrac{1}{2}\varepsilon = \int_a^b f + \varepsilon, \quad \text{for all } n > N.$$

Since $U(f, P_n) \geq \int_a^b f$, by the definition of the integral, we deduce that

$$\left| U(f, P_n) - \int_a^b f \right| = U(f, P_n) - \int_a^b f < \varepsilon, \quad \text{for all } n > N.$$

Hence $\lim_{n \to \infty} U(f, P_n) = \int_a^b f$, as required. ∎

Our next result is a converse to Theorem 1.2, but its proof is easier.

Theorem 1.3 Let f be a bounded function on $[a, b]$. If there is a sequence of partitions P_n of $[a, b]$ such that $\|P_n\| \to 0$ and

$$\lim_{n \to \infty} L(f, P_n) = \lim_{n \to \infty} U(f, P_n) = I, \tag{1.6}$$

where $I \in \mathbb{R}$, then f is integrable on $[a, b]$ and $\int_a^b f = I$.

See Frame 15.

Proof   Let $\varepsilon > 0$. It follows from equations (1.6) that there exists an integer n such that

$$L(f, P_n) > I - \tfrac{1}{2}\varepsilon \quad \text{and} \quad U(f, P_n) < I + \tfrac{1}{2}\varepsilon. \tag{1.7}$$

Now, by the definitions of upper and lower integrals,

$$\underline{\int_a^b} f \geq L(f, P_n) \quad \text{and} \quad \overline{\int_a^b} f \leq U(f, P_n). \tag{1.8}$$

Combining inequalities (1.7) and (1.8), we obtain

$$I - \tfrac{1}{2}\varepsilon < \underline{\int_a^b} f \leq \overline{\int_a^b} f < I + \tfrac{1}{2}\varepsilon.$$

Since ε is any positive number, we deduce that the upper and lower integrals of f on $[a, b]$ are equal to I, so f is integrable and

$$\int_a^b f = I. \quad \blacksquare$$

The inequality

$$\underline{\int_a^b} f \leq \overline{\int_a^b} f$$

follows from Theorem 1.1.

We can now deduce *Riemann's Criterion* for integrability.

Corollary   Riemann's Criterion

Let f be bounded on $[a, b]$. Then

$\qquad f$ is integrable on $[a, b]$

if and only if

$\qquad$ there is a sequence $\{P_n\}$ of partitions of $[a, b]$ with $\|P_n\| \to 0$
$\qquad$ such that $U(f, P_n) - L(f, P_n) \to 0$.

Proof   Theorem 1.2 implies that if f is integrable on $[a, b]$, then there is a sequence P_n of partitions of $[a, b]$ with $\|P_n\| \to 0$ such that $U(f, P_n) - L(f, P_n) \to 0$.

On the other hand, if there is a sequence P_n of partitions of $[a, b]$ with $\|P_n\| \to 0$ such that $U(f, P_n) - L(f, P_n) \to 0$, then, because

$$L(f, P_n) \leq \underline{\int_a^b} f \leq \overline{\int_a^b} f \leq U(f, P_n),$$

these upper and lower integrals must be equal, so f is integrable on $[a, b]$, by Theorem 1.3. $\quad \blacksquare$

Manipulating integrals

The audio frames stated several rules for manipulating integrals. Here, we briefly mention some key ideas needed in the proofs of these rules, without giving much detail.

Additivity of integrals

The statements about additivity of integrals can all be proved using Riemann's Criterion, by fairly routine arguments.

See Frame 19.

Sign of an integral

The statements

See Frame 20.

$$f(x) \geq 0 \Rightarrow \int_a^b f \geq 0 \quad \text{and} \quad f(x) \leq 0 \Rightarrow \int_a^b f \leq 0,$$

follow from the definition of the integral.

Modulus Rule

$$\int_a^b f \text{ exists} \Rightarrow \int_a^b |f| \text{ exists}.$$

See Frame 21.

A proof of this rule can be given using the following quantity: for a bounded function f on $[a,b]$ and a partition

$$P = \{[x_0, x_1], [x_1, x_2], \dots, [x_{n-1}, x_n]\},$$

of $[a,b]$, we define, for $i = 1, 2, \dots, n$, the **variation** $\omega_i(f)$ of f over the subinterval $[x_{i-1}, x_i]$ to be

$$\omega_i(f) = \sup\{|f(x) - f(y)| : x, y \in [x_{i-1}, x_i]\}.$$

It can be shown that

$$\omega_i(f) = \sup\{f(x) : x_{i-1} \leq x \leq x_i\} - \inf\{f(x) : x_{i-1} \leq x \leq x_i\},$$

so

$$U(f, P) - L(f, P) = \sum_{i=1}^{n} \omega_i(f) \, \delta x_i, \tag{1.9}$$

where $\delta x_i = x_i - x_{i-1}$, as usual.

Now, by the Triangle Inequality (backwards form),

See Unit AA1, Section 3.

$$\big||f(x)| - |f(y)|\big| \leq |f(x) - f(y)|, \quad \text{for } x, y \in [x_{i-1}, x_i],$$

so

$$\omega_i(|f|) \leq \omega_i(f), \quad \text{for } i = 1, 2, \dots, n.$$

Hence, by equation (1.9),

$$U(|f|, P) - L(|f|, P) \leq U(f, P) - L(f, P), \tag{1.10}$$

for any partition P of $[a,b]$. We can now use Riemann's Criterion to deduce from inequality (1.10) that if f is integrable on $[a,b]$, then so is $|f|$.

Combination Rules

To prove the Combination Rules, we can use the same approach as for the Modulus Rule. Here we need the following inequalities, which relate the variations of the new functions over a subinterval $[x_{i-1}, x_i]$ of a partition to those of the known integrable functions f and g:

See Frame 22.

$$\omega_i(f + g) \leq \omega_i(f) + \omega_i(g),$$
$$\omega_i(\lambda f) \leq |\lambda| \, \omega_i(f), \quad \text{for } \lambda \in \mathbb{R},$$
$$\omega_i(fg) \leq M(\omega_i(f) + \omega_i(g)), \quad \text{where } M = \max\{\sup|f|, \sup|g|\}.$$

Sufficient conditions for integrability

Finally, we use Riemann's Criterion to prove that monotonic functions and continuous functions are integrable.

See Frame 23.

> **Theorem 1.4**   A function f which is bounded and monotonic on $[a, b]$ is integrable on $[a, b]$.

Proof   We prove this theorem in the case when f is increasing on $[a, b]$.

The proof is similar if f is decreasing.

Consider the *standard* partition of $[a, b]$; that is,

$$P_n = \{[x_0, x_1], [x_1, x_2], \ldots, [x_{n-1}, x_n]\}, \tag{1.11}$$

where

$$x_i = a + i\,\frac{b-a}{n}, \quad \text{for } i = 0, 1, 2, \ldots, n. \tag{1.12}$$

Now f is increasing, so on each subinterval $[x_{i-1}, x_i]$, for $i = 1, 2, \ldots, n$,

$$m_i = f(x_{i-1}) \quad \text{and} \quad M_i = f(x_i).$$

Also, $\delta x_i = (b-a)/n$, for $i = 1, 2, \ldots, n$. Hence

$$U(f, P_n) - L(f, P_n) = \sum_{i=1}^{n}(M_i - m_i)\,\delta x_i$$

$$= \frac{b-a}{n}\sum_{i=1}^{n}(f(x_i) - f(x_{i-1}))$$

$$= \frac{b-a}{n}(f(x_n) - f(x_0))$$

$$= \frac{b-a}{n}(f(b) - f(a)).$$

The terms of this series are
$$f(x_1) - f(x_0),$$
$$f(x_2) - f(x_1),$$
$$\vdots$$
$$f(x_n) - f(x_{n-1}),$$
so most terms cancel.

The sequence $\{(b-a)(f(b) - f(a))/n\}$ is null, so it follows from Riemann's Criterion that f is integrable on $[a, b]$. ∎

> **Theorem 1.5**   A function f which is continuous on $[a, b]$ is integrable on $[a, b]$.

Proof   We use the fact that f must be uniformly continuous on $[a, b]$.

See Unit AB1, Theorem 4.2.

Let $\varepsilon > 0$. Then there exists $\delta > 0$ such that

$$|f(x) - f(y)| < \frac{\varepsilon}{b-a}, \quad \text{for all } x, y \in [a, b] \text{ with } |x - y| < \delta. \tag{1.13}$$

We use $\varepsilon/(b-a)$ here in order to obtain ε later in the proof.

Next we choose $N \in \mathbb{N}$ such that $(b-a)/N < \delta$. For $n \geq N$, let P_n be the standard partition of $[a, b]$ given by equations (1.11) and (1.12).

Now f is continuous on each $[x_{i-1}, x_i]$, for $i = 1, 2, \ldots, n$. Thus, by the Extreme Value Theorem, there exist points c_i and d_i in $[x_{i-1}, x_i]$ such that

See Unit AA4, Theorem 3.3.

$$m_i = f(c_i) \quad \text{and} \quad M_i = f(d_i). \tag{1.14}$$

Since $[x_{i-1}, x_i]$ has length $(b-a)/n < \delta$, we deduce by statements (1.13) and (1.14) that

$$M_i - m_i < \frac{\varepsilon}{b-a}.$$

Hence, for $n \geq N$ we have

$$U(f, P_n) - L(f, P_n) = \sum_{i=1}^{n} (M_i - m_i)\, \delta x_i$$

$$< \sum_{i=1}^{n} \left(\frac{\varepsilon}{b-a} \right) \left(\frac{b-a}{n} \right) = \varepsilon.$$

Thus $U(f, P_n) - L(f, P_n)$ is a null sequence, so it follows from Riemann's Criterion that f is integrable on $[a, b]$.   ∎

Remark   Theorems 1.4 and 1.5 show that monotonic functions and continuous functions are integrable, but we know that some bounded functions are not integrable: for example, the Dirichlet function. This suggests the question: precisely which bounded functions are integrable?

See Frame 13.

The full answer to this question is rather complicated but, roughly speaking, a bounded function is integrable on $[a, b]$ if and only if it is continuous at 'most' points of $[a, b]$. However, it is possible for a function to be discontinuous at infinitely many points of $[a, b]$ and yet be integrable on $[a, b]$. For example, the Riemann function is discontinuous at all rational points and yet it can be shown to be integrable on $[0, 1]$, the value of its integral being 0.

See Unit AB1, Section 3.

Further exercises

Exercise 1.3 Sketch the graph of the function

$$f(x) = \begin{cases} 1 - |x|, & -1 < x < 1, \\ 1, & x = \pm 1. \end{cases}$$

Determine (if they exist) the minimum, maximum, infimum and supremum of f on $[-1, 1]$.

Exercise 1.4 Let f be the function

$$f(x) = \begin{cases} |x|, & -1 < x < 1, \\ \frac{1}{2}, & x = \pm 1. \end{cases}$$

Evaluate $L(f, P)$ and $U(f, P)$ for each of the following partitions P of $[-1, 1]$.

(a) $P = \left\{ [-1, -\frac{1}{2}], [-\frac{1}{2}, 0], [0, \frac{1}{2}], [\frac{1}{2}, 1] \right\}$

(b) $P = \left\{ [-1, -\frac{1}{4}], [-\frac{1}{4}, \frac{1}{3}], [\frac{1}{3}, 1] \right\}$

Exercise 1.5 Let f be the function

$$f(x) = \begin{cases} 1 - x, & 0 \leq x < 1, \\ 2, & x = 1. \end{cases}$$

(a) Using the standard partition P_n of $[0, 1]$, evaluate $L(f, P_n)$ and $U(f, P_n)$.

(b) Deduce that f is integrable on $[0, 1]$, and evaluate $\int_0^1 f$.

Exercise 1.6 Use Theorem 1.3 to prove that the constant function

$$f(x) = c \quad (x \in [a, b])$$

is integrable on $[a, b]$ and

$$\int_a^b f = (b - a)c.$$

Exercise 1.7 Prove that the function
$$f(x) = \begin{cases} 1 + x, & 0 \le x \le 1, \ x \text{ rational}, \\ 1 - x, & 0 \le x \le 1, \ x \text{ irrational}, \end{cases}$$
is not integrable on $[0, 1]$.

Exercise 1.8 Prove that if the functions f and g are integrable on $[a, b]$, then so is the function $\max\{f, g\}$.

Hint: $\max\{f(x), g(x)\} = \frac{1}{2}\big(f(x) + g(x) + |f(x) - g(x)|\big)$.

2   Evaluation of integrals

After working through this section, you should be able to:

(a) explain what is meant by a *primitive* of a function and understand the Fundamental Theorem of Calculus;

(b) use the Fundamental Theorem of Calculus and the table of standard primitives to evaluate certain integrals;

(c) use *integration by substitution* and *integration by parts*;

(d) use the *reduction of order* method to evaluate certain integrals.

2.1   Fundamental Theorem of Calculus

We can often evaluate integrals without the need for upper and lower Riemann sums, by using the idea of a *primitive*.

Definition   Let f be a function defined on an interval I. Then a function F is a **primitive** of f on I if F is differentiable on I and
$$F'(x) = f(x), \quad \text{for } x \in I.$$

To avoid introducing a name, such as F, we can denote a primitive of f by $\int f(x)\, dx$; we do not always specify the interval I.

Alternative names for primitive are *indefinite integral* and *antiderivative*.

Note that the domain of F may be larger than I.

Finding a primitive is the inverse of finding a derivative. For example, if
$$f(x) = \tan x,$$
then the function
$$F(x) = \log_e(\sec x)$$
is a primitive of f on the interval $\left(-\frac{1}{2}\pi, \frac{1}{2}\pi\right)$, since
$$F'(x) = \frac{1}{\sec x}\sec x \tan x = \tan x, \quad \text{for } x \in \left(-\tfrac{1}{2}\pi, \tfrac{1}{2}\pi\right).$$

Thus we can write
$$\int \tan x\, dx = \log_e(\sec x),$$
on the interval $\left(-\frac{1}{2}\pi, \frac{1}{2}\pi\right)$.

Exercise 2.1

(a) Let
$$f(x) = (x^2 - 4)^{-1/2} \quad (x \in (2, \infty)).$$
Prove that
$$F(x) = \log_e(x + (x^2 - 4)^{1/2})$$
is a primitive of f on $(2, \infty)$.

(b) Let
$$f(x) = \operatorname{sech} x.$$

Prove that
$$F(x) = \tan^{-1}(\sinh x)$$

is a primitive of f on $\mathbb{R}$.

Recall that
$$\operatorname{sech} x = \frac{1}{\cosh x}.$$

One of the facts which makes calculus such an important subject is that differentiation and integration are inverse processes. The following result shows that we can evaluate the integral of a function f on an interval I by finding a primitive of f on I.

Theorem 2.1 Fundamental Theorem of Calculus

Let f be integrable on $[a, b]$ and let F be a primitive of f on $[a, b]$. Then

$$\int_a^b f = F(b) - F(a).$$

Often $F(b) - F(a)$ is written as
$$[F(x)]_a^b \quad \text{or} \quad F(x)|_a^b.$$

Proof   Let
$$P_n = \{[x_0, x_1], \ldots, [x_{i-1}, x_i], \ldots, [x_{n-1}, x_n]\}, \quad n = 1, 2, \ldots,$$

be any sequence of partitions of $[a, b]$, with $\|P_n\| \to 0$.

On each subinterval
$$[x_{i-1}, x_i], \quad \text{for } i = 1, 2, \ldots, n,$$

the function F satisfies the conditions of the Mean Value Theorem. Hence there exists a point $c_i \in (x_{i-1}, x_i)$ such that

$$F(x_i) - F(x_{i-1}) = F'(c_i)(x_i - x_{i-1})$$
$$= f(c_i)\,\delta x_i, \tag{2.1}$$

where $\delta x_i = x_i - x_{i-1}$. Since
$$m_i \le f(c_i) \le M_i, \quad \text{for } i = 1, 2, \ldots, n,$$

it follows that

$$\sum_{i=1}^n m_i\,\delta x_i \le \sum_{i=1}^n f(c_i)\,\delta x_i \le \sum_{i=1}^n M_i\,\delta x_i.$$

Using equation (2.1), we can rewrite this statement as

$$L(f, P_n) \le \sum_{i=1}^n (F(x_i) - F(x_{i-1})) \le U(f, P_n).$$

The middle series has sum $F(x_n) - F(x_0) = F(b) - F(a)$, so

$$L(f, P_n) \le F(b) - F(a) \le U(f, P_n). \tag{2.2}$$

Since f is integrable on $[a, b]$, the sequences $\{L(f, P_n)\}$ and $\{U(f, P_n)\}$ both converge to $\int_a^b f$, by Theorem 1.2. It follows from statement (2.2) and the Limit Inequality Rule for sequences that

$$\int_a^b f \le F(b) - F(a) \le \int_a^b f;$$

this gives the required result.   ■

If you are short of time, omit this proof.

See Unit AB2, Theorem 4.1.

Recall (from Frame 2) that
$$m_i = \inf\{f(x) : x \in [x_{i-1}, x_i]\},$$
$$M_i = \sup\{f(x) : x \in [x_{i-1}, x_i]\}.$$

The terms of this series are
$$F(x_1) - F(x_0),$$
$$F(x_2) - F(x_1),$$
$$\vdots$$
$$F(x_n) - F(x_{n-1}).$$

See Unit AA2, Section 3.

Theorem 2.1 shows the close relationship between the integral $\int_a^b f$ and any primitive F of f on $[a, b]$. This explains why a primitive F is also called an *indefinite* integral of f, and why the notation $\int f(x)\, dx$ is used. Moreover, the process of finding a primitive of f is often informally called *integrating* f, and in this context the function f is called an **integrand**.

Also, the integral $\int_a^b f$ is often called the *definite integral* of f over $[a, b]$.

We can use Theorem 2.1 and the table of standard primitives to evaluate many integrals.

This table is on page 53.

Example 2.1   Evaluate $\displaystyle\int_0^1 2^x\, dx$.

In this example, the integrand is the function $x \longmapsto 2^x$.

Solution   The function $f(x) = 2^x$ has the following primitive on $[0, 1]$:

$$F(x) = 2^x / \log_e 2.$$

Hence, by the Fundamental Theorem of Calculus,

$$\int_0^1 2^x\, dx = \left[\frac{2^x}{\log_e 2} \right]_0^1 = \frac{2}{\log_e 2} - \frac{1}{\log_e 2} = \frac{1}{\log_e 2}. \quad \blacksquare$$

Exercise 2.2   Using the table of standard primitives, evaluate the following integrals.

(a) $\displaystyle\int_0^4 (x^2 + 9)^{1/2}\, dx$ (b) $\displaystyle\int_1^e \log_e x\, dx$

2.2 Primitives

It is natural to ask: can a function have more than one primitive on an interval? The answer to this question is 'yes': for example, on $(-1, 1)$ the functions

$$x \longmapsto \sin^{-1} x \quad \text{and} \quad x \longmapsto -\cos^{-1} x$$

are both primitives of the function

$$x \longmapsto (1 - x^2)^{-1/2}.$$

However, any two primitives of a function f on an interval can differ only by a constant.

In the above example,
$$\sin^{-1} x = \tfrac{1}{2}\pi - \cos^{-1} x.$$

Theorem 2.2 Uniqueness Theorem for Primitives

Let F_1 and F_2 be primitives of f on an interval I. Then there exists some constant c such that

$$F_2(x) = F_1(x) + c, \quad \text{for } x \in I.$$

This theorem states that a primitive of a function on an interval is unique, apart from adding an *arbitrary constant*.

Proof   Since F_1 and F_2 are primitives of f on I,

$$F_1'(x) = f(x) \quad \text{and} \quad F_2'(x) = f(x), \quad \text{for } x \in I,$$

so

$$F_2'(x) - F_1'(x) = 0, \quad \text{for } x \in I.$$

Thus, by the Zero Derivative Theorem, there exists a constant c such that

$$F_2(x) - F_1(x) = c, \quad \text{for } x \in I. \quad \blacksquare$$

See Unit AB2, the corollary to Theorem 4.2.

The range of primitives we can find is considerably extended by the use of several Combination Rules.

Combination Rules Let F and G be primitives of f and g, respectively, on an interval I, and $\lambda \in \mathbb{R}$. Then, on I:

Sum Rule $f + g$ has a primitive $F + G$;

Multiple Rule λf has a primitive λF;

Scaling Rule $x \longmapsto f(\lambda x)$ has a primitive $x \longmapsto \dfrac{1}{\lambda} F(\lambda x)$.

These rules are proved using the corresponding rules for derivatives.

For example, it follows from the table of standard primitives and the Combination Rules that the function with domain $\mathbb{R}^+$ and rule

$$x \longmapsto 3x^{-1} + \sinh 2x$$

has a primitive

$$x \longmapsto 3\log_e x + \tfrac{1}{2}\cosh 2x.$$

In applications of these Combination Rules we do not usually mention the rules explicitly.

Exercise 2.3 Using the table of standard primitives and the Combination Rules, find a primitive of each of the following functions.

(a) $f(x) = 4\log_e x - 2/(4 + x^2)$ $(x \in (0, \infty))$

(b) $f(x) = 2\tan 3x + e^{2x}\cos x$ $(x \in (-\tfrac{1}{6}\pi, \tfrac{1}{6}\pi))$

2.3 Techniques of integration

The Fundamental Theorem of Calculus provides a powerful method for evaluating certain integrals. However, even when we know that a function f has a primitive F, it may not be possible to determine F explicitly.

In fact, most functions f, even simple ones, have primitives which are not standard functions, but are new functions of no previously known type. For example, the primitives

$$\int e^{-x^2}\, dx \quad \text{and} \quad \int \frac{dx}{(\log_e x)^2}$$

cannot be expressed as a combination of a finite number of rational, nth root, trigonometric, exponential and logarithmic functions.

Note this shorthand way of writing

$$\int \frac{1}{(\log_e x)^2}\, dx.$$

Using the Combination Rules, we can integrate any *polynomial* function, and the primitive is always another polynomial function. For example,

$$\int (x^2 - x + 5)\, dx = \tfrac{1}{3}x^3 - \tfrac{1}{2}x^2 + 5x.$$

Also, there is a standard procedure for integrating a *rational* function, and any primitive of a rational function can always be expressed in terms of rational functions, logarithms of rational functions and inverse tangents of linear functions.

This procedure, called the method of *partial fractions*, is often used for evaluating the integrals of rational functions in complex analysis. It is not used in this course.

There are also various techniques which can be applied to certain other types of function; the art of integration lies in recognising these types. We now describe briefly some basic techniques of integration.

Integration by substitution

Our first substitution technique is used when the integrand is of the form

$$x \longmapsto f(g(x))g'(x).$$

In this case, if F is a primitive of f, then

$$\frac{d}{dx}F(g(x)) = F'(g(x)g'(x) = f(g(x))g'(x) \quad \text{(by the Chain Rule)}.$$

Thus $x \longmapsto F(g(x))$ is a primitive of $x \longmapsto f(g(x))g'(x)$ on any interval in the domain of $F \circ g$. Thus, if we substitute $u = g(x)$, then

$$\int f(g(x))g'(x)\,dx = F(g(x)) = F(u) = \int f(u)\,du. \qquad (2.3)$$

This technique is worth trying if you can express the integrand in the form $f(g(x))g'(x)$, for some functions f and g.

Strategy 2.1   To find a primitive

$$\int f(g(x))g'(x)\,dx,$$

using integration by substitution.

1. Choose $u = g(x)$; find $\dfrac{du}{dx} = g'(x)$ and express du in terms of x and dx.

2. Substitute $u = g(x)$ and replace $g'(x)\,dx$ by du (adjusting constants if necessary) to give $\int f(u)\,du$.

3. Find $\int f(u)\,du$.

4. Substitute $u = g(x)$ to give the required primitive.

Example   Find

$$\int x^2(x^3 + 1)^8\,dx.$$

1. Put $u = g(x) = x^3 + 1$. Then
$$\frac{du}{dx} = g'(x) = 3x^2, \quad \text{so} \quad du = 3x^2\,dx.$$

2. $\displaystyle\int x^2(x^3+1)^8\,dx = \tfrac{1}{3}\int (x^3+1)^8\, 3x^2\,dx$
$$= \tfrac{1}{3}\int u^8\,du.$$

3. $\displaystyle \tfrac{1}{3}\int u^8\,du = \tfrac{1}{3} \times \tfrac{1}{9}u^9 = \tfrac{1}{27}u^9.$

4. $\displaystyle\int x^2(x^3+1)^8\,dx = \tfrac{1}{27}(x^3+1)^9.$

Remarks

1. If we are evaluating an integral, rather than finding a primitive, then there is no need to perform step 4. Instead, we can change the x-limits of integration into the corresponding u-limits:

    $$\int_a^b f(g(x))g'(x)\,dx = \int_{g(a)}^{g(b)} f(u)\,du.$$

2. When applying equation (2.3), you may be able to spot a primitive F of f immediately, so you can write down the required primitive $F(g(x))$ directly without need for a substitution. For example,

    $$\int x^2(x^3+1)^8\,dx = \tfrac{1}{3}\int (x^3+1)^8\, 3x^2\,dx$$

    $$= \tfrac{1}{3} \times \tfrac{1}{9}(x^3+1)^9 = \tfrac{1}{27}(x^3+1)^9.$$

    This situation occurs with an integrand of the form $g'(x)/g(x)$ on an interval I, since we have

    $$\int \frac{g'(x)}{g(x)}\,dx = \log_e(g(x)), \quad \text{if } g(x) > 0, \quad \text{for } x \in I. \qquad (2.4)$$

In the above example,
$$u = g(x) = x^3 + 1,$$
so
when $x = 0$, $u = 1$,
when $x = 1$, $u = 2$.
Hence
$$\int_0^1 x^2(x^3+1)^8\,dx$$
$$= \tfrac{1}{3}\int_1^2 u^8\,du.$$

If $F(x) = \log_e(g(x))$, then
$$F'(x) = \frac{g'(x)}{g(x)}.$$

An example of this useful formula appears in the next exercise.

Exercise 2.4   Find a primitive of each of the following functions.

(a) $f(x) = \sin(\sin 3x)\cos 3x \quad (x \in \mathbb{R})$

(b) $f(x) = x^2(2 + 3x^3)^7 \quad (x \in \mathbb{R})$

(c) $f(x) = x\sin(2x^2) \quad (x \in \mathbb{R})$

(d) $f(x) = x/(2 + 3x^2) \quad (x \in \mathbb{R})$

Exercise 2.5   Evaluate the integral

$$\int_0^1 \frac{e^x}{(1 + e^x)^2}\,dx.$$

Our second substitution technique is a modification of the above method, which we call *backwards substitution*. It is based on the formula

$$\int f(x)\,dx = \int f(h(u))h'(u)\,du,$$

obtained from equation (2.3) by swapping the variables x and u. Here h is a function such that $x = h(u)$, often found by first writing $u = g(x)$ where g has an inverse function $g^{-1} = h$. Backwards substitution is worth trying if it makes part of the integrand significantly simpler.

Strategy 2.2   To find a primitive

$$\int f(x)\,dx,$$

using integration by backwards substitution.

1. Choose $u = g(x)$, where g has an inverse function $x = h(u)$, and express dx in terms of u and du.

2. Substitute $x = h(u)$ and replace dx by $h'(u)\,du$ to give a primitive in terms of u.

3. Find this primitive.

4. Substitute $u = g(x)$ to give the required primitive.

Example   Find

$$\int \frac{e^{2x}}{(e^x - 1)^{1/2}}\,dx.$$

1. Put $u = g(x) = (e^x - 1)^{1/2}$, so $x = h(u) = \log_e(u^2 + 1)$. Then

$$\frac{dx}{du} = h'(u) = \frac{2u}{u^2 + 1}, \quad \text{so} \quad dx = \frac{2u}{u^2 + 1}\,du.$$

2. $$\int \frac{e^{2x}}{(e^x - 1)^{1/2}}\,dx = \int \frac{(u^2 + 1)^2}{u}\,\frac{2u}{u^2 + 1}\,du$$

$$= \int 2(u^2 + 1)\,du.$$

3. $$\int 2(u^2 + 1)\,du = \tfrac{2}{3}u^3 + 2u.$$

4. $$\int \frac{e^{2x}}{(e^x - 1)^{1/2}}\,dx = \tfrac{2}{3}(e^x - 1)^{3/2} + 2(e^x - 1)^{1/2}.$$

Remark   As before, if we are evaluating an integral, then, instead of step 4, we can change the x-limits of integration into the corresponding u-limits:

$$\int_a^b f(x)\,dx = \int_{g(a)}^{g(b)} f(g^{-1}(u))(g^{-1})'(u)\,du.$$

In the above example,

$$u = g(x) = (e^x - 1)^{1/2},$$

so

when $x = 0$, $\quad u = 0$,

when $x = 1$, $\quad u = \sqrt{e - 1}$.

Hence

$$\int_0^1 \frac{e^{2x}}{(e^x - 1)^{1/2}}\,dx$$

$$= \int_0^{\sqrt{e-1}} 2(u^2 + 1)\,du.$$

Exercise 2.6

(a) Find a primitive of the function

$$f(x) = \frac{1}{3(x-1)^{3/2} + x(x-1)^{1/2}} \quad (x \in (1, \infty)),$$

using the substitution $u = (x-1)^{1/2}$.

(b) Evaluate the integral

$$\int_0^{\log_e 3} e^x \sqrt{1 + e^x} \, dx.$$

Integration by parts

The technique of *integration by parts* is derived from the Product Rule for differentiation,

$$(fg)' = f'g + fg',$$

which implies that

$$\int fg' = fg - \int f'g, \quad \text{so} \quad \int_a^b fg' = [fg]_a^b - \int_a^b f'g.$$

This formula converts the problem of finding a primitive of fg' into the problem of finding a primitive of $f'g$. Integration by parts is worth trying if you can express the integrand as a product of two functions, $f(x)g'(x)$, where $f(x)$ becomes simpler on differentiation, and $g'(x)$ becomes not much more complicated on integration.

Strategy 2.3   To find a primitive

$$\int k(x) \, dx,$$

using integration by parts.

1. Write the original function k in the form fg', where f is a function that you can differentiate and g' is a function that you can integrate.

2. Use the formula

$$\int fg' = fg - \int f'g.$$

Example   Find

$$\int x \cos x \, dx.$$

1. Take $f(x) = x$, $g'(x) = \cos x$; then $f'(x) = 1$, $g(x) = \sin x$.

2. Hence

$$\int x \cos x \, dx = x \sin x - \int \sin x \, dx$$

$$= x \sin x + \cos x.$$

Sometimes we have to multiply the integrand by the factor 1 in order to be able to apply integration by parts, as in the following example.

Example 2.2   Evaluate the integral

$$\int_0^1 \tan^{-1} x \, dx.$$

Solution   We use integration by parts, introducing the factor 1:

$$\int_0^1 \tan^{-1} x \, dx = \int_0^1 1 \times \tan^{-1} x \, dx$$

$$= \left[x \tan^{-1} x \right]_0^1 - \int_0^1 \frac{x}{1 + x^2} \, dx$$

$$= \tan^{-1} 1 - \left[\tfrac{1}{2} \log_e(1 + x^2) \right]_0^1$$

$$= \tfrac{1}{4}\pi - (\tfrac{1}{2}\log_e 2 - \tfrac{1}{2}\log_e 1) = \tfrac{1}{4}\pi - \tfrac{1}{2}\log_e 2. \quad \blacksquare$$

Here

$$f(x) = \tan^{-1} x, \quad g'(x) = 1,$$

so

$$f'(x) = \frac{1}{1 + x^2}, \quad g(x) = x.$$

Here we use equation (2.4) with $g(x) = 1 + x^2$.

Exercise 2.7

(a) Find a primitive of the function
$$k(x) = x^{1/3} \log_e x \quad (x \in \mathbb{R}^+).$$

(b) Evaluate the integral
$$\int_0^{\pi/2} x^2 \cos x \, dx.$$

Hint: Use integration by parts twice.

Reduction of order

Sometimes we need to evaluate an integral I_n that involves a non-negative integer n. A common approach to such integrals is to relate the value of I_n to the value of I_{n-1} or I_{n-2} by a *reduction formula*, using integration by parts. Here is an example that will be important later in the unit.

This is another name for a recurrence relation.

Example 2.3   Let
$$I_n = \int_0^{\pi/2} \sin^n x \, dx, \quad n = 0, 1, 2, \dots.$$

(a) Evaluate I_0 and I_1.

(b) Prove that
$$I_n = \left(\frac{n-1}{n}\right) I_{n-2}, \quad \text{for } n \geq 2.$$

(c) Deduce the values of I_2, I_3, I_4 and I_5.

Solution

(a) We have $I_0 = \int_0^{\pi/2} 1 \, dx = \pi/2$ and
$$I_1 = \int_0^{\pi/2} \sin x \, dx = \left[-\cos x\right]_0^{\pi/2} = 1.$$

(b) We write
$$I_n = \int_0^{\pi/2} \sin x \, \sin^{n-1} x \, dx.$$

Using integration by parts we find that, for $n \geq 2$,

We integrate $\sin x$ and differentiate $\sin^{n-1} x$.

$$I_n = \left[(-\cos x) \sin^{n-1} x\right]_0^{\pi/2} - \int_0^{\pi/2} (-\cos x)(n-1) \sin^{n-2} x \cos x \, dx$$

$$= 0 + (n-1) \int_0^{\pi/2} \cos^2 x \sin^{n-2} x \, dx$$

$$= (n-1) \int_0^{\pi/2} (1 - \sin^2 x) \sin^{n-2} x \, dx$$

$$= (n-1) \left(\int_0^{\pi/2} \sin^{n-2} x \, dx - \int_0^{\pi/2} \sin^n x \, dx\right)$$

$$= (n-1)(I_{n-2} - I_n).$$

We can rearrange this equation to give
$$nI_n = (n-1)I_{n-2}, \quad \text{so} \quad I_n = \left(\frac{n-1}{n}\right) I_{n-2}, \quad \text{for } n \geq 2.$$

(c) Using the result of part (b) with $n = 2, 3, 4, 5$ in turn, we obtain

$$I_2 = \frac{1}{2}I_0 = \frac{1}{2} \cdot \frac{\pi}{2} = \frac{\pi}{4},$$

$$I_3 = \frac{2}{3}I_1 = \frac{2}{3},$$

$$I_4 = \frac{3}{4}I_2 = \frac{3}{4} \cdot \frac{\pi}{4} = \frac{3\pi}{16},$$

$$I_5 = \frac{4}{5}I_3 = \frac{4}{5} \cdot \frac{2}{3} = \frac{8}{15}. \quad \blacksquare$$

Remark   Repeatedly applying the reduction formula in Example 2.3, we obtain the general formulas

$$I_{2n} = \frac{1}{2} \cdot \frac{3}{4} \cdot \frac{5}{6} \cdot \ldots \cdot \frac{2n-1}{2n} \cdot \frac{\pi}{2}$$

and

$$I_{2n+1} = \frac{2}{3} \cdot \frac{4}{5} \cdot \frac{6}{7} \cdot \ldots \cdot \frac{2n}{2n+1}.$$

We use these formulas in Subsection 3.2.

Exercise 2.8   Let

$$I_n = \int_0^1 e^x x^n \, dx, \quad n = 0, 1, 2, \ldots.$$

(a) Evaluate I_0.

(b) Prove that

$$I_n = e - nI_{n-1}, \quad \text{for } n = 1, 2, \ldots.$$

(c) Deduce the values of I_1, I_2, I_3 and I_4.

Further exercises

Exercise 2.9   Write down a primitive $F(x)$ of each of the following functions.

(a) $f(x) = (x^2 - 9)^{1/2} \quad (x \in (3, \infty))$

(b) $f(x) = \sin(2x + 3) - 4\cos(3x - 2) \quad (x \in \mathbb{R})$

(c) $f(x) = e^{2x} \sin 3x \quad (x \in \mathbb{R})$

Exercise 2.10   For the function f in Exercise 2.9(c), write down a primitive F for which $F(\pi) = 0$.

Exercise 2.11 Evaluate each of the following integrals, using the suggested substitution where given.

(a) $\displaystyle\int_0^{\pi/2} \tan(\sin x)\cos x\,dx, \quad u = \sin x.$

(b) $\displaystyle\int_0^1 \frac{(\tan^{-1} x)^2}{1 + x^2}\,dx, \quad u = \tan^{-1} x.$

(c) $\displaystyle\int_0^{\pi/2} \frac{\sin 2x}{1 + 3\cos^2 x}\,dx$

(d) $\displaystyle\int_1^e 8x^7 \log_e x\,dx$

(e) $\displaystyle\int_e^{e^2} \frac{\log_e(\log_e x)}{x}\,dx$

(f) $\displaystyle\int_1^4 \frac{dx}{(1 + x)\sqrt{x}}, \quad u = \sqrt{x}.$

(g) $\displaystyle\int_0^{\pi/2} \frac{dx}{2 + \cos x}, \quad u = \tan(\tfrac{1}{2}x).$

Hint: In part (g), use the identity

$$\cos x = \frac{\cos^2(\tfrac{1}{2}x) - \sin^2(\tfrac{1}{2}x)}{\cos^2(\tfrac{1}{2}x) + \sin^2(\tfrac{1}{2}x)} = \frac{1 - \tan^2(\tfrac{1}{2}x)}{1 + \tan^2(\tfrac{1}{2}x)}.$$

Exercise 2.12 Let

$$I_n = \int_1^e x(\log_e x)^n\,dx, \quad n = 0, 1, 2, \ldots.$$

(a) Prove that

$$I_n = \tfrac{1}{2}e^2 - \tfrac{1}{2}nI_{n-1}, \quad \text{for } n = 1, 2, \ldots.$$

(b) Evaluate I_0, I_1, I_2 and I_3.

3   Inequalities, sequences and series

After working through this section, you should be able to:

(a) determine lower and upper estimates for given integrals;

(b) state Wallis' Formula;

(c) use the Integral Test to determine the convergence or divergence of certain series.

Often it is not possible to evaluate an integral explicitly, and a numerical estimate for its value is sufficient. This can occur both in applications of mathematics and in proofs that involve integration. In this section we study some inequalities satisfied by integrals, and apply these to find a remarkable formula for π and to decide whether certain series are convergent or divergent.

Finding accurate estimates for the values of difficult integrals is part of the subject of numerical analysis.

3.1 Inequalities for integrals

The basic inequality rules for integrals are as follows.

Inequality Rules   Let f and g be integrable on $[a, b]$.

(a) If $f(x) \leq g(x)$, for $x \in [a, b]$, then

$$\int_a^b f \leq \int_a^b g.$$

(b) If $m \leq f(x) \leq M$, for $x \in [a, b]$, then

$$m(b - a) \leq \int_a^b f \leq M(b - a).$$

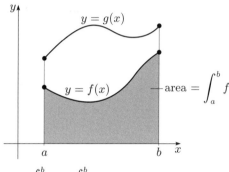

(a) $\int_a^b f \leq \int_a^b g$

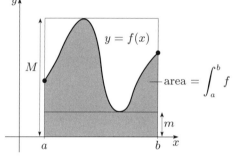

(b) $m(b - a) \leq \int_a^b f \leq M(b - a)$

Proof

(a) Let P be a partition of $[a, b]$. Since

$$f(x) \leq g(x), \quad \text{for } x \in [a, b],$$

the infimum of f on each subinterval of P is less than or equal to the infimum of g on that subinterval, so $L(f, P) \leq L(g, P)$. Thus

$$\int_a^b f = \sup_P\{L(f, P)\} \leq \sup_P\{L(g, P)\} = \int_a^b g,$$

since f and g are both integrable on $[a, b]$.

(b) Since $f(x) \leq M$ for $x \in [a, b]$, it follows from part (a), with $g(x) = M$, that

$$\int_a^b f \leq \int_a^b M \, dx = M(b - a).$$

The proof of the left-hand inequality is similar.   ∎

The Inequality Rules allow us to estimate a complicated integral by evaluating a simpler one, as in the next example.

Example 3.1   Prove the following inequalities.

(a) $\displaystyle \int_0^1 \frac{x^3}{2 - \sin^4 x} \, dx \leq \tfrac{1}{4} \log_e 2$ (b) $\displaystyle \frac{3}{\sqrt{34}} \leq \int_{-1}^2 \frac{dx}{\sqrt{2 + x^5}} \leq 3$

Solution

(a) Since

$$|\sin x| \le |x|, \quad \text{for } x \in \mathbb{R},$$

it follows that

$$\sin^4 x \le x^4, \quad \text{for } x \in \mathbb{R}.$$

Thus $2 - \sin^4 x \ge 2 - x^4 > 0$ for $x \in [0, 1]$, so

$$\frac{x^3}{2 - \sin^4 x} \le \frac{x^3}{2 - x^4}, \quad \text{for } x \in [0, 1].$$

Hence, by Inequality Rule(a), we have

$$\int_0^1 \frac{x^3}{2 - \sin^4 x}\, dx \le \int_0^1 \frac{x^3}{2 - x^4}\, dx$$
$$= \left[-\tfrac{1}{4} \log_e (2 - x^4)\right]_0^1$$
$$= -\tfrac{1}{4}(\log_e 1 - \log_e 2) = \tfrac{1}{4} \log_e 2.$$

(b) Since the function $x \longmapsto \sqrt{2 + x^5}$ is increasing on $[-1, 2]$, we have

$$1 \le \sqrt{2 + x^5} \le \sqrt{34}, \quad \text{for } x \in [-1, 2],$$

so

$$\frac{1}{\sqrt{34}} \le \frac{1}{\sqrt{2 + x^5}} \le 1, \quad \text{for } x \in [-1, 2].$$

Since the length of the interval $[-1, 2]$ is 3, it follows from Inequality Rule(b) that

$$\frac{3}{\sqrt{34}} \le \int_{-1}^2 \frac{dx}{\sqrt{2 + x^5}} \le 3. \quad \blacksquare$$

> **Exercise 3.1** Use the Inequality Rules to prove the following inequalities.
>
> (a) $\displaystyle\int_1^3 x \sin\left(1/x^{10}\right) dx \le 4$ (b) $\dfrac{1}{2} \le \displaystyle\int_0^{1/2} e^{x^2}\, dx \le \tfrac{1}{2} e^{1/4}$

We noted earlier that if the function f is integrable on $[a, b]$, then so also is $|f|$. We now use the Inequality Rules to obtain an inequality involving the integrals of f and $|f|$.

Triangle Inequality Let f be integrable on $[a, b]$. Then

$$\left| \int_a^b f \right| \le \int_a^b |f|.$$

Furthermore, if $|f(x)| \le M$ for $x \in [a, b]$, then

$$\left| \int_a^b f \right| \le M(b - a).$$

See Unit AA4, Section 2, the corollary to the Sine Inequality.

Here we use equation (2.4) with $g(x) = 2 - x^4$.

See Subsection 1.2, Frame 21.

The name arises because of the similarity between this inequality and the Triangle Inequality for numbers:

$$\left| \sum_{i=1}^n a_i \right| \le \sum_{i=1}^n |a_i|.$$

Proof   We know that

$$-|f(x)| \leq f(x) \leq |f(x)|.$$

Since $|f|$ is integrable on $[a, b]$, it follows from Inequality Rule(a) that

$$-\int_a^b |f| \leq \int_a^b f \leq \int_a^b |f|,$$

which is equivalent to

$$\left| \int_a^b f \right| \leq \int_a^b |f|.$$

Finally, if $|f(x)| \leq M$ for $x \in [a, b]$, then, by the above inequality and Inequality Rule(b),

$$\left| \int_a^b f \right| \leq \int_a^b |f| \leq M(b - a). \quad \blacksquare$$

Sometimes we use a mixture of these rules, as in the next example.

Example 3.2   Prove that

$$\left| \int_0^{\pi/2} \frac{x - \pi/2}{2 + \cos x} \, dx \right| \leq \frac{\pi^2}{16}.$$

Solution   By the Triangle Inequality for integrals,

$$\left| \int_0^{\pi/2} \frac{x - \pi/2}{2 + \cos x} \, dx \right| \leq \int_0^{\pi/2} \left| \frac{x - \pi/2}{2 + \cos x} \right| \, dx$$

$$= \int_0^{\pi/2} \frac{\pi/2 - x}{2 + \cos x} \, dx. \qquad (3.1)$$

For $0 \leq x \leq \pi/2$, we have
$$x - \pi/2 \leq 0$$
and
$$\cos x \geq 0.$$

Since

$$2 + \cos x \geq 2, \quad \text{for } x \in [0, \pi/2],$$

we have

$$\frac{1}{2 + \cos x} \leq \frac{1}{2}, \quad \text{for } x \in [0, \pi/2].$$

Thus, by Inequality Rule(a) and statement (3.1),

$$\left| \int_0^{\pi/2} \frac{x - \pi/2}{2 + \cos x} \, dx \right| \leq \int_0^{\pi/2} \frac{1}{2} \left(\frac{\pi}{2} - x \right) \, dx$$

$$= \frac{1}{2} \left[\frac{\pi}{2} x - \frac{1}{2} x^2 \right]_0^{\pi/2}$$

$$= \frac{1}{2} \left(\frac{\pi^2}{4} - \frac{\pi^2}{8} \right) = \frac{\pi^2}{16}. \quad \blacksquare$$

Exercise 3.2   Prove the following inequalities.

(a) $\left| \displaystyle\int_1^4 \frac{\sin(1/x)}{2 + \cos(1/x)} \, dx \right| \leq 3$ (b) $\left| \displaystyle\int_0^{\pi/4} \frac{\tan x}{3 - \sin(x^2)} \, dx \right| \leq \frac{1}{4} \log_e 2$

3.2 Wallis' Formula

In Example 2.3 we used a reduction formula to show that if

$$I_n = \int_0^{\pi/2} \sin^n x \, dx, \quad n = 0, 1, 2, \ldots,$$

then

$$I_0 = \frac{\pi}{2}, \quad I_1 = 1 \quad \text{and} \quad I_n = \left(\frac{n-1}{n}\right) I_{n-2}, \quad \text{for } n \geq 2. \tag{3.2}$$

We also remarked that

$$I_{2n} = \frac{1}{2} \cdot \frac{3}{4} \cdot \frac{5}{6} \cdot \cdots \cdot \frac{2n-1}{2n} \cdot \frac{\pi}{2}, \quad \text{for } n \geq 1, \tag{3.3}$$

and

$$I_{2n+1} = \frac{2}{3} \cdot \frac{4}{5} \cdot \frac{6}{7} \cdot \cdots \cdot \frac{2n}{2n+1}, \quad \text{for } n \geq 1. \tag{3.4}$$

Note that the formula for I_{2n} involves π, but the formula for I_{2n+1} does not.

We now use these results, together with inequalities between various integrals of the form I_n, to establish two remarkable formulas for π.

Wallis' Formula

(a) $\displaystyle \lim_{n \to \infty} \left(\frac{2}{1} \cdot \frac{2}{3} \cdot \frac{4}{3} \cdot \frac{4}{5} \cdot \frac{6}{5} \cdot \frac{6}{7} \cdot \cdots \cdot \frac{2n}{2n-1} \cdot \frac{2n}{2n+1}\right) = \frac{\pi}{2}$

(b) $\displaystyle \lim_{n \to \infty} \frac{(n!)^2 \, 2^{2n}}{(2n)! \sqrt{n}} = \sqrt{\pi}$

John Wallis (1616–1703) was an English mathematician whose work on 'infinite arithmetic' influenced Newton in his discovery of calculus. Both of these limits are called Wallis' Formula.

The next exercise includes an identity needed in the proof of Wallis' Formula.

Exercise 3.3   For $n = 1, 2, \ldots$, let

$$a_n = \frac{2}{1} \cdot \frac{2}{3} \cdot \frac{4}{3} \cdot \frac{4}{5} \cdot \frac{6}{5} \cdot \frac{6}{7} \cdot \cdots \cdot \frac{2n}{2n-1} \cdot \frac{2n}{2n+1} \quad \text{and} \quad b_n = \frac{(n!)^2 \, 2^{2n}}{(2n)! \sqrt{n}}.$$

(a) Evaluate a_n and b_n, for $n = 1, 2, 3$.

(b) Verify that

$$b_n^2 = \left(\frac{2n+1}{n}\right) a_n, \quad \text{for } n = 1, 2, 3.$$

(c) Prove that

$$b_n^2 = \left(\frac{2n+1}{n}\right) a_n, \quad \text{for } n = 1, 2, \ldots.$$

Proof of Wallis' Formula

If you are short of time, omit this proof.

Let

$$I_n = \int_0^{\pi/2} \sin^n x \, dx, \quad n = 0, 1, 2, \ldots,$$

and let the sequences $\{a_n\}$ and $\{b_n\}$ be as given in Exercise 3.3.

(a) Using equations (3.3) and (3.4), we obtain, for $n \geq 1$,

$$\frac{I_{2n}}{I_{2n+1}} = \frac{1 \cdot 3 \cdot 3 \cdot 5 \cdot \cdots \cdot (2n-1)(2n+1)}{2 \cdot 2 \cdot 4 \cdot 4 \cdot \cdots \cdot (2n)(2n)} \frac{\pi}{2} = \frac{1}{a_n} \cdot \frac{\pi}{2},$$

so

$$a_n = \left(\frac{I_{2n+1}}{I_{2n}} \right) \frac{\pi}{2}.$$

Thus, to prove part (a) of Wallis' Formula, it is sufficient to show that

$$\frac{I_{2n+1}}{I_{2n}} \to 1 \quad \text{as } n \to \infty. \tag{3.5}$$

We do this as follows. Since $0 \le \sin x \le 1$, for $x \in [0, \pi/2]$, we have

$$\sin^{2n} x \ge \sin^{2n+1} x \ge \sin^{2n+2} x, \quad \text{for } x \in [0, \pi/2].$$

It follows by Inequality Rule(a) that

$$I_{2n} \ge I_{2n+1} \ge I_{2n+2}.$$

Thus, on dividing by I_{2n}, we obtain

$$1 \ge \frac{I_{2n+1}}{I_{2n}} \ge \frac{I_{2n+2}}{I_{2n}} = \frac{2n+1}{2n+2}, \tag{3.6}$$

by equation (3.2). On taking the limit as $n \to \infty$ in statement (3.6), we deduce that equation (3.5) holds, by the Squeeze Rule for sequences.   See Unit AA2, Section 3.

(b) We know, from Exercise 3.3(c), that

$$b_n^2 = \left(\frac{2n+1}{n} \right) a_n = \left(2 + \frac{1}{n} \right) a_n.$$

By part (a),

$$a_n \to \frac{\pi}{2} \quad \text{as } n \to \infty,$$

so, by the Product Rule for sequences,

$$b_n^2 \to 2 \times \frac{\pi}{2} = \pi \quad \text{as } n \to \infty.$$

Hence, by the continuity of the square root function,

$$b_n \to \sqrt{\pi} \quad \text{as } n \to \infty. \quad \blacksquare$$

3.3 Integral Test

In this section we introduce a method based on integration for determining the convergence or divergence of certain series of the form $\sum\limits_{n=1}^{\infty} f(n)$, where the function f is positive and decreasing and tends to 0. The method is based on the fact that it is often easier to evaluate an integral than a sum which has a similar behaviour.

Integral Test   Let the function f be positive and decreasing on $[1, \infty)$, and suppose that $f(x) \to 0$ as $x \to \infty$. Then

(a) $\sum\limits_{n=1}^{\infty} f(n)$ converges if the sequence $\left\{ \int_1^n f \right\}$ is bounded above;

(b) $\sum\limits_{n=1}^{\infty} f(n)$ diverges if $\int_1^n f \to \infty$ as $n \to \infty$.

The Integral Test is also called the *Maclaurin Integral Test*.

In both these results, the number 1 can be replaced by any positive integer.

Proof   For $n = 2, 3, \ldots$, let $s_n = f(1) + f(2) + \cdots + f(n)$ be the nth partial sum of the series, and let P_{n-1} be the standard partition of $[1, n]$ with $n - 1$ subintervals:

$$\{[1, 2], \ldots, [i, i+1], \ldots, [n-1, n]\}.$$

Since f is decreasing on $[1, \infty)$, we have, for $i = 1, 2, \ldots, n-1$,

$$m_i = f(i+1) \quad \text{and} \quad M_i = f(i).$$

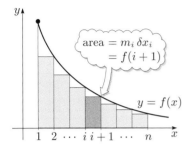

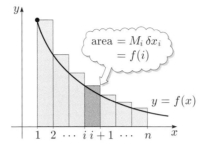

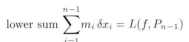

lower sum $\displaystyle\sum_{i=1}^{n-1} m_i \, \delta x_i = L(f, P_{n-1})$ upper sum $\displaystyle\sum_{i=1}^{n-1} M_i \, \delta x_i = U(f, P_{n-1})$

Also, each subinterval in the partition has length 1. Hence the lower and upper Riemann sums for f on $[1, n]$ are

$$L(f, P_{n-1}) = \sum_{i=1}^{n-1} m_i \times 1 = f(2) + \cdots + f(n) = s_n - f(1)$$

and

$$U(f, P_{n-1}) = \sum_{i=1}^{n-1} M_i \times 1 = f(1) + \cdots + f(n-1) = s_n - f(n).$$

Since f is monotonic on $[1, n]$, the integral $I_n = \int_1^n f$ exists and satisfies   See Theorem 1.4.

$$L(f, P_{n-1}) \leq I_n \leq U(f, P_{n-1}),$$

so

$$s_n - f(1) \leq I_n \leq s_n - f(n). \tag{3.7}$$

Case (a): The sequence $\{I_n\}$ is bounded above.

In this case, there exists $M \in \mathbb{R}$ such that

$$I_n \leq M, \quad \text{for } n = 2, 3, \ldots.$$

It follows from the left-hand inequality in statement (3.7) that

$$s_n \leq f(1) + M, \quad \text{for } n = 2, 3, \ldots.$$

Thus the increasing sequence $\{s_n\}$ is bounded above, so it is convergent, by the Monotone Convergence Theorem.   See Unit AA2, Section 5.

Hence the series $\displaystyle\sum_{n=1}^{\infty} f(n)$ is convergent.

Case (b): The sequence $\{I_n\}$ is not bounded above.

The sequence $\{I_n\}$ is increasing, since

$$I_{n+1} - I_n = \int_n^{n+1} f \geq 0,$$

so in this case

$$I_n \to \infty \ \text{ as } n \to \infty.$$

It follows from the right-hand inequality in statement (3.7) that

$$s_n \geq I_n, \quad \text{for } n = 2, 3, \ldots.$$

Thus, by the Squeeze Rule for sequences which tend to infinity,

See Unit AA2, Section 4.

$$s_n \to \infty \ \text{ as } n \to \infty.$$

Hence the series $\displaystyle\sum_{n=1}^{\infty} f(n)$ is divergent. ∎

Earlier in the course, we showed that the basic series $\displaystyle\sum_{n=1}^{\infty} 1/n^p$ converges

See Unit AA3, Subsection 2.2.

for $p \geq 2$ and diverges for $0 < p \leq 1$. We can now deduce the behaviour of this series for all $p > 0$.

Example 3.3   Use the Integral Test to determine the behaviour of the series

$$\sum_{n=1}^{\infty} \frac{1}{n^p}, \quad \text{for } p > 0, \ p \neq 1.$$

The case $p = 1$ is considered in Exercise 3.4(a).

Solution   Let $p > 0$ and $p \neq 1$, and let

$$f(x) = 1/x^p \quad (x \in [1, \infty)).$$

Then f is positive and decreasing on $[1, \infty)$, and

$$f(x) \to 0 \ \text{ as } x \to \infty.$$

Also, for $n \in \mathbb{N}$,

$$\int_1^n f = \int_1^n \frac{dx}{x^p} = \left[\frac{x^{1-p}}{1-p}\right]_1^n = \frac{n^{1-p} - 1}{1 - p}. \tag{3.8}$$

First suppose that $p > 1$. Then $p - 1 > 0$, so equation (3.8) gives

$$\int_1^n f = \frac{1}{p-1}\left(1 - \frac{1}{n^{p-1}}\right) < \frac{1}{p-1}.$$

Hence the sequence $\left\{\int_1^n f\right\}$ is bounded above, so it follows from the Integral Test that the series converges.

Now suppose that $0 < p < 1$. Then $1 - p > 0$, so $1/n^{1-p} \to 0$ as $n \to \infty$, and hence

$$n^{1-p} \to \infty \ \text{ as } n \to \infty,$$

by the Reciprocal Rule for sequences. We deduce from equation (3.8) that

See Unit AA2, Section 4.

$$\int_1^n f \to \infty \ \text{ as } n \to \infty.$$

Hence, by the Integral Test, the series diverges. ∎

Exercise 3.4

(a) Use the fact that $\displaystyle\int \frac{dx}{x} = \log_e x$ to prove that

$$\sum_{n=1}^{\infty} \frac{1}{n} \text{ is divergent.}$$

(b) Show that

$$\int \frac{dx}{x(\log_e x)^2} = -\frac{1}{\log_e x},$$

and hence prove that

$$\sum_{n=2}^{\infty} \frac{1}{n(\log_e n)^2} \text{ is convergent.}$$

Further exercises

Exercise 3.5 Prove the following inequalities.

(a) $\int_0^1 x^3 \sqrt{2(1+x^{99})}\, dx \leq \frac{1}{2}$ (b) $\int_0^1 \frac{x^4}{(1+3x^{97})^{1/2}}\, dx \geq \frac{1}{10}$

Exercise 3.6 Prove the following inequalities.

(a) $\frac{1}{2} \leq \int_0^1 \frac{1+x^{30}}{2-x^{99}}\, dx \leq 2$ (b) $\left| \int_0^2 \frac{x^2(x-3)\sin 9x}{1+x^{20}}\, dx \right| \leq 4$

Exercise 3.7

(a) Show that

$$\int \frac{dx}{x(\log_e x)^{3/2}} = -2(\log_e x)^{-1/2},$$

and hence prove that

$$\sum_{n=2}^{\infty} \frac{1}{n(\log_e n)^{3/2}} \text{ is convergent.}$$

(b) Show that

$$\int \frac{dx}{x \log_e x} = \log_e(\log_e x),$$

and hence prove that

$$\sum_{n=2}^{\infty} \frac{1}{n \log_e n} \text{ is divergent.}$$

4 Stirling's Formula

After working through this section, you should be able to:

(a) understand the connection between integration and Stirling's Formula for $n!$;

(b) use Stirling's Formula to determine the behaviour of certain sequences involving factorials.

In this section we use the notation $\sim$ to represent a way of comparing the behaviour of positive functions of n for large values of n.

In Unit I3 we used the notation $\sim$ for a general equivalence relation. Here $\sim$ is a *particular* equivalence relation. We read $\sim$ as 'twiddles'.

Definition   For positive functions f and g with domain $\mathbb{N}$, we write

$$f(n) \sim g(n) \quad \text{as } n \to \infty$$

to mean

$$\frac{f(n)}{g(n)} \to 1 \quad \text{as } n \to \infty.$$

Often we omit 'as $n \to \infty$'.

For example,

$$n^2 + n \sim n^2 \quad \text{as } n \to \infty,$$

since $n^2 + n > 0$ and $n^2 > 0$, for $n = 1, 2, \ldots$, and

$$\frac{n^2 + n}{n^2} \to 1 \quad \text{as } n \to \infty.$$

In essence, $\sim$ compares the sizes of the *dominant terms* in $f(n)$ and $g(n)$. Note that the statement

$$f(n) \sim g(n) \quad \text{as } n \to \infty$$

does *not* imply that $f(n) - g(n)$ tends to zero or is even bounded. For instance, in the above example, $(n^2 + n) - n^2 = n$ tends to infinity.

We have the following Combination Rules for $\sim$.

Combination Rules   If $f_1(n) \sim g_1(n)$ and $f_2(n) \sim g_2(n)$, then:

Sum Rule $f_1(n) + f_2(n) \sim g_1(n) + g_2(n)$;

Multiple Rule $\lambda f_1(n) \sim \lambda g_1(n)$, for $\lambda \in \mathbb{R}^+$;

Product Rule $f_1(n) f_2(n) \sim g_1(n) g_2(n)$;

Quotient Rule $\dfrac{f_1(n)}{f_2(n)} \sim \dfrac{g_1(n)}{g_2(n)}.$

These rules follow from the Combination Rules for sequences. We omit the details.

Remark   If $l > 0$, then the statements

$$f(n) \to l \quad \text{as } n \to \infty$$

and

$$f(n) \sim l \quad \text{as } n \to \infty$$

are equivalent, since each is equivalent to the statement

$$\frac{f(n)}{l} \to 1 \quad \text{as } n \to \infty.$$

4.1 Calculating factorials

For small values of n, we can evaluate $n!$ directly by multiplication or by using a scientific calculator.

Exercise 4.1   Complete the following table of values of $n!$.

n	$n!$	n	$n!$	n	$n!$
1	1	6	720	20	$2.432\ldots \times 10^{18}$
2	2	7	5 040	30	
3	6	8	40 320	40	
4	24	9	362 880	50	
5	120	10	3 628 800	60	

As n increases, $n!$ grows very quickly, and is soon beyond the range of a calculator. Many calculations in probability theory involve $n!$ for large values of n, so it is important to be able to estimate this quantity as accurately as possible. The main aim of the video programme is to prove the following estimate of $n!$ for large values of n, known as *Stirling's Formula*:

$$n! \sim \sqrt{2\pi n}\,(n/e)^n \quad \text{as } n \to \infty.$$

Exercise 4.2   Use your calculator to evaluate $\sqrt{2\pi n}\,(n/e)^n$ for the following values of n.

(a) $n = 5$ (b) $n = 10$ (c) $n = 50$

In the programme we use two facts from probability theory to illustrate how Stirling's Formula can be used.

1. There are 52! ways of dealing (in different orders) a pack of 52 cards.
2. If 200 coins are tossed, then the probability of obtaining exactly 100 heads and 100 tails is

$$\binom{200}{100}\left(\frac{1}{2}\right)^{200} = \frac{200!}{(100!)^2\,2^{200}}.$$

We state these facts without proof.

Watch the video programme 'Heads and Tails'.

4.2 Review of the video programme

We begin the programme with a reminder of the two formulas from probability theory given in Subsection 4.1.

Next, we review the definition of the integral in terms of lower and upper Riemann sums; we also prove that monotonic functions are integrable and that $\displaystyle\sum_{n=1}^{\infty} 1/n$ diverges, whereas $\displaystyle\sum_{n=1}^{\infty} 1/n^2$ converges.

The main part of the programme consists of a proof of Stirling's Formula, based on geometric properties of the graph $y = \log_e x$.

Stirling's Formula

$$n! \sim \sqrt{2\pi n}\,(n/e)^n \quad \text{as } n \to \infty.$$

James Stirling (1692–1770) was a Scottish mathematician who made many contributions to analysis. This formula appeared in his textbook on analysis *Methodus Differentialis*, published in 1730. It was also known to Abraham de Moivre, who wrote extensively on 'the laws of chance'.

Proof   Consider the function

$$f(x) = \log_e x.$$

For $n = 2, 3, \ldots$, let P_{n-1} be the standard partition of the interval $[1, n]$ with $n - 1$ subintervals:

$$\{[1, 2], \ldots, [i, i + 1], \ldots, [n - 1, n]\}.$$

Now consider the sequence $\{c_n\}_2^\infty$, where c_n is the total area of the set which lies between the graph

$$y = \log_e x, \quad x \in [1, n],$$

and the 'polygonal' graph with vertices

$$(1, 0), \quad (2, \log_e 2), \quad (3, \log_e 3), \quad \ldots, \quad (n, \log_e n),$$

as illustrated below. This set consists of $n - 1$ thin segments.

The function f is concave (that is, its derivative is decreasing), so the line segment joining

$$(i, \log_e i) \text{ to } (i + 1, \log_e (i + 1))$$

lies below the graph $y = \log_e x$.

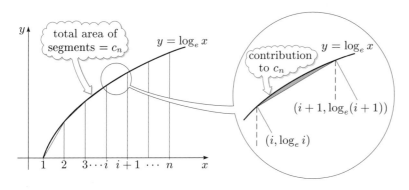

The area of the set between $y = \log_e x$, $x \in [1, n]$, and the x-axis is

$$\int_1^n \log_e x \, dx = \left[x \log_e x - x \right]_1^n$$
$$= n \log_e n - (n - 1). \tag{4.1}$$

The area between the polygonal graph and the x-axis is

$$\tfrac{1}{2}(L(f, P_{n-1}) + U(f, P_{n-1})). \tag{4.2}$$

Since f is increasing, we have

$$L(f, P_{n-1}) = \log_e 1 + \log_e 2 + \cdots + \log_e(n - 1)$$
$$= \log_e(n - 1)!$$
$$= \log_e(n!/n) = \log_e n! - \log_e n \tag{4.3}$$

and

$$U(f, P_{n-1}) = \log_e 2 + \log_e 3 + \cdots + \log_e n$$
$$= \log_e n!. \tag{4.4}$$

Substituting from equations (4.3) and (4.4) into equation (4.2), we find that the area between the polygonal graph and the x-axis is

$$\tfrac{1}{2}(\log_e n! - \log_e n + \log_e n!) = \log_e n! - \tfrac{1}{2} \log_e n. \tag{4.5}$$

It follows from equations (4.1) and (4.5) that

$$c_n = n \log_e n - (n - 1) - \log_e n! + \tfrac{1}{2} \log_e n$$
$$= \log_e \left(\frac{n^{n+(1/2)}}{e^{n-1} n!} \right).$$

The sequence $\{c_n\}$ is positive and increasing. Also,

$$c_n \le \log_e 2, \quad \text{for } n \in \mathbb{N},$$

since the $n-1$ segments which contribute to the area c_n can be translated so that they all lie (without overlapping) in the triangle with vertices $(1,0)$, $(1, \log_e 2)$ and $(2, \log_e 2)$, as illustrated. This geometric property holds because the function $\log_e$ is concave. It follows from the Monotone Convergence Theorem that the sequence $\{c_n\}$ is convergent.

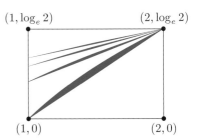

Next, since the exponential function is continuous, the sequence

$$a_n = e^{c_n}, \quad n = 2, 3, \ldots,$$

is convergent also. Thus

$$a_n = \frac{n^{n+(1/2)}}{e^{n-1} n!} \to L \quad \text{as } n \to \infty, \tag{4.6}$$

for some non-zero number L.

To find L, we consider the quotient

$$\frac{a_n^2}{a_{2n}} = \frac{n^{2n+1}}{e^{2n-2}(n!)^2} \bigg/ \frac{(2n)^{2n+(1/2)}}{e^{2n-1}(2n)!} = \frac{(2n)! \, n^{1/2}}{(n!)^2 \, 2^{2n}} \times \frac{e}{\sqrt{2}}.$$

We now let $n \to \infty$ in this equation. We have

$$a_n \to L, \quad a_{2n} \to L \quad \text{and} \quad \frac{(2n)! \, n^{1/2}}{(n!)^2 \, 2^{2n}} \to \frac{1}{\sqrt{\pi}},$$

by Wallis' Formula. Hence

$$\frac{L^2}{L} = \frac{1}{\sqrt{\pi}} \times \frac{e}{\sqrt{2}}, \quad \text{so} \quad L = \frac{e}{\sqrt{2\pi}}.$$

Wallis' Formula is
$$\lim_{n \to \infty} \frac{(n!)^2 \, 2^{2n}}{(2n)! \sqrt{n}} = \sqrt{\pi};$$
see page 33.

Thus we can rewrite statement (4.6) in the form

$$a_n = \frac{n^{n+(1/2)}}{e^{n-1} n!} \to \frac{e}{\sqrt{2\pi}} \quad \text{as } n \to \infty.$$

Hence, by the Combination Rules for sequences,

$$\frac{e^n n!}{n^n \sqrt{n}} \to \sqrt{2\pi} \quad \text{as } n \to \infty,$$

which can be rearranged to give Stirling's Formula:

$$n! \sim \sqrt{2\pi n} \, (n/e)^n \quad \text{as } n \to \infty. \quad \blacksquare$$

Even for small values of n, Stirling's Formula gives reasonable approximations to $n!$, and the relative error decreases as n increases.

n	$n!$	Stirling's approximation	Relative error
10	$3\,628\,800$	$3\,598\,696$	0.83%
20	2.433×10^{18}	2.423×10^{18}	0.42%
52	8.066×10^{67}	8.053×10^{67}	0.16%
100	9.333×10^{157}	9.325×10^{157}	0.08%

Remark   It can be shown by a more careful argument that

$$e^{1/(12n+1)} \leq \frac{n!}{\sqrt{2\pi n} \, (n/e)^n} \leq e^{1/(12n)}, \quad \text{for } n \geq 1.$$

For example, if $n = 10$, then

$$e^{1/(12n+1)} = e^{1/121} = 1.008\,29 \ldots \quad \text{and} \quad e^{1/(12n)} = e^{1/120} = 1.008\,36 \ldots,$$

which indicate a relative error of about 0.8%, as shown in the above table.

Finally in the programme, we see that if we toss 200 coins, then the probability of obtaining exactly 100 heads and 100 tails is

$$\frac{200!}{(100!)^2\,2^{200}} \simeq \frac{\sqrt{400\pi}\,(200/e)^{200}}{\left(\sqrt{200\pi}\,(100/e)^{100}\right)^2 2^{200}}$$

$$= \frac{\sqrt{400\pi}\,(200^{200}/e^{200})}{200\pi\,(100^{200}/e^{200})\,2^{200}}$$

$$= \frac{\sqrt{400\pi}}{200\pi}$$

$$= \frac{1}{10\sqrt{\pi}} = \frac{1}{17.724\ldots},$$

rather higher than you might expect.

Here we substitute $n = 200$ and then $n = 100$ into Stirling's Formula.

In calculations based on Stirling's formula, such extensive cancellation of factors often occurs.

4.3 Using Stirling's Formula

Exercise 4.3   Use Stirling's Formula to estimate each of the following numbers (giving your answers to two significant figures).

(a) $\dbinom{300}{150}\dfrac{1}{2^{300}}$ (b) $\dfrac{300!}{(100!)^3}\dfrac{1}{3^{300}}$

In some of these exercises, you will need to use the Combination Rules for $\sim$; see page 38.

Exercise 4.4   Use Stirling's Formula to determine a number λ such that

$$\dbinom{4n}{2n}\bigg/\dbinom{2n}{n} \sim \lambda 2^{2n} \quad \text{as } n \to \infty.$$

Exercise 4.5   Use Stirling's Formula to prove that

$$\lim_{n\to\infty}\left(\frac{n^n}{n!}\right)^{1/n} = e.$$

Hint: You can assume that if $f(n) \sim g(n)$, then $(f(n))^{1/n} \sim (g(n))^{1/n}$.

This result about $\sim$ holds because if $n \in \mathbb{N}$, then

$$a \le a^{1/n} < 1, \quad \text{for } 0 < a < 1,$$

and

$$1 < a^{1/n} \le a, \quad \text{for } a > 1,$$

by the rules for inequalities.

Further exercises

Exercise 4.6   Use Stirling's Formula to estimate each of the following numbers (giving your answers to two significant figures).

(a) $\dbinom{400}{200}\left(\dfrac{1}{2}\right)^{400}$ (b) $\dfrac{400!\sqrt{800\pi}}{(100!)^4\,4^{400}}$

Exercise 4.7   Use Stirling's Formula to determine a number λ such that

$$\frac{(8n)!}{((2n)!)^4} \sim \lambda \frac{4^{8n-1}}{n^{3/2}} \quad \text{as } n \to \infty.$$

Exercise 4.8   Use Stirling's Formula to prove that

$$\dbinom{3n}{n} \sim \sqrt{\frac{3}{4\pi n}}\,\frac{3^{3n}}{2^{2n}} \quad \text{as } n \to \infty.$$

Solutions to the exercises

1.1 (a)

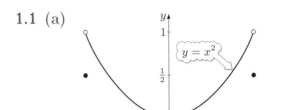

$\min\{f(x) : x \in [-1,1]\} = 0$, since
1. $f(x) \geq 0$, for all $x \in [-1,1]$,
2. $f(0) = 0$.

$\inf\{f(x) : x \in [-1,1]\} = 0$, since

f has minimum 0 on $[-1,1]$.

$\sup\{f(x) : x \in [-1,1]\} = 1$, since
1. $f(x) \leq 1$, for all $x \in [-1,1]$,
2. if $M' < 1$, then M' is not an upper bound for f on $[-1,1]$ because the sequence $\{1 - 1/n\}$ is contained in $[-1,1]$ and
$$f(1 - 1/n) = (1 - 1/n)^2 \to 1 \quad \text{as } n \to \infty.$$
(Alternatively, consider $f(-1 + 1/n)$.)

$\max\{f(x) : x \in [-1,1]\}$ does not exist, since

there is no point x such that $f(x) = 1$.

(b)

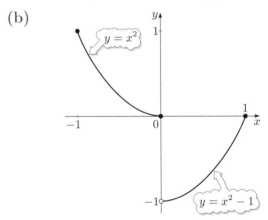

$\inf\{f(x) : x \in [-1,1]\} = -1$, since
1. $f(x) \geq -1$, for all $x \in [-1,1]$,
2. if $m' > -1$, then m' is not a lower bound for f on $[-1,1]$ because the sequence $\{1/n\}$ is contained in $[-1,1]$ and
$$f(1/n) = (1/n)^2 - 1 \to -1 \quad \text{as } n \to \infty.$$

$\min\{f(x) : x \in [-1,1]\}$ does not exist, since

there is no point x such that $f(x) = -1$.

$\max\{f(x) : x \in [-1,1]\} = 1$, since
1. $f(x) \leq 1$, for all $x \in [-1,1]$,
2. $f(-1) = 1$.

$\sup\{f(x) : x \in [-1,1]\} = 1$, since

f has maximum 1 on $[-1,1]$.

1.2 (a)

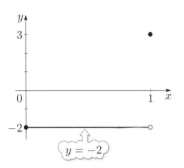

Let P_n be the standard partition of $[0,1]$:
$$\left\{ \left[0, \frac{1}{n}\right], \left[\frac{1}{n}, \frac{2}{n}\right], \ldots, \left[\frac{n-1}{n}, 1\right] \right\}.$$
For $i = 1, 2, \ldots, n$, we have
$$m_i = \inf\{f(x) : (i-1)/n \leq x \leq i/n\} = -2.$$
For $i = 1, 2, \ldots, n-1$, we have
$$M_i = \sup\{f(x) : (i-1)/n \leq x \leq i/n\} = -2.$$
Also, $M_n = 3$ and
$$\delta x_i = \frac{1}{n}, \quad \text{for } i = 1, 2, \ldots, n.$$
Hence
$$L(f, P_n) = \sum_{i=1}^{n} m_i \, \delta x_i$$
$$= \sum_{i=1}^{n} \left(-2 \times \frac{1}{n}\right)$$
$$= n \times \left(\frac{-2}{n}\right) = -2,$$
$$U(f, P_n) = \sum_{i=1}^{n} M_i \, \delta x_i$$
$$= \sum_{i=1}^{n-1} M_i \, \delta x_i + M_n \, \delta x_n$$
$$= \sum_{i=1}^{n-1} \left(-2 \times \frac{1}{n}\right) + \left(3 \times \frac{1}{n}\right)$$
$$= (n-1)\left(\frac{-2}{n}\right) + \frac{3}{n}$$
$$= -2 + \frac{5}{n} \to -2 \quad \text{as } n \to \infty.$$
Since $\|P_n\| \to 0$ as $n \to \infty$, and
$$\lim_{n \to \infty} L(f, P_n) = \lim_{n \to \infty} U(f, P_n) = -2,$$
it follows from Theorem 1.3 that f is integrable on $[0,1]$ and
$$\int_0^1 f = -2.$$

(b)

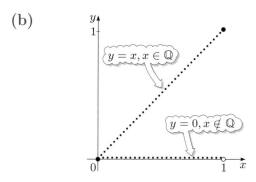

Let P_n be the standard partition of $[0,1]$:

$$\left\{\left[0,\frac{1}{n}\right],\left[\frac{1}{n},\frac{2}{n}\right],\ldots,\left[\frac{n-1}{n},1\right]\right\}.$$

Each subinterval

$$\left[\frac{i-1}{n},\frac{i}{n}\right],\quad\text{for } i=1,2,\ldots,n,$$

contains both rational and irrational points:

at the rational points, $f(x)=x$,
at the irrational points, $f(x)=0$.

Hence, for $i=1,2,\ldots,n$,

$$m_i=0\quad\text{and}\quad M_i=\frac{i}{n}.$$

Also,

$$\delta x_i=\frac{1}{n},\quad\text{for } i=1,2,\ldots,n.$$

Hence

$$L(f,P_n)=\sum_{i=1}^{n}m_i\,\delta x_i$$
$$=\sum_{i=1}^{n}\left(0\times\frac{1}{n}\right)=0,$$

$$U(f,P_n)=\sum_{i=1}^{n}M_i\,\delta x_i$$
$$=\sum_{i=1}^{n}\left(\frac{i}{n}\times\frac{1}{n}\right)$$
$$=\frac{1}{n^2}\sum_{i=1}^{n}i$$
$$=\frac{1}{n^2}\times\frac{n(n+1)}{2}$$
$$=\frac{1}{2}+\frac{1}{2n}\to\frac{1}{2}\quad\text{as } n\to\infty.$$

Since $\|P_n\|\to 0$ as $n\to\infty$, but

$$\lim_{n\to\infty}L(f,P_n)=0\neq\tfrac{1}{2}=\lim_{n\to\infty}U(f,P_n),$$

it follows from Theorem 1.2 that f is not integrable on $[0,1]$.

1.3

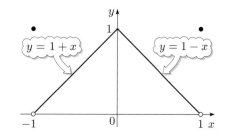

$\inf\{f(x):x\in[-1,1]\}=0$, since

1. $f(x)\geq 0$, for all $x\in[-1,1]$,
2. if $m'>0$, then m' is not a lower bound for f on $[-1,1]$ because the sequence $\{1-1/n\}$ is contained in $[-1,1]$ and
$$f(1-1/n)=1-(1-1/n)$$
$$=\frac{1}{n}\to 0\quad\text{as } n\to\infty.$$

$\min\{f(x):x\in[-1,1]\}$ does not exist, since there is no point x such that $f(x)=0$.

$\max\{f(x):x\in[-1,1]\}=1$, since

1. $f(x)\leq 1$, for all $x\in[-1,1]$,
2. $f(-1)=f(0)=f(1)=1$.

$\sup\{f(x):x\in[-1,1]\}=1$, since

f has maximum 1 on $[-1,1]$.

1.4

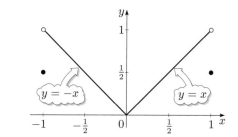

(a) $L(f,P)=\sum_{i=1}^{4}m_i\,\delta x_i$
$$=\left(\tfrac{1}{2}\times\tfrac{1}{2}\right)+\left(0\times\tfrac{1}{2}\right)+\left(0\times\tfrac{1}{2}\right)+\left(\tfrac{1}{2}\times\tfrac{1}{2}\right)$$
$$=\tfrac{1}{2}$$

$U(f,P)=\sum_{i=1}^{4}M_i\,\delta x_i$
$$=\left(1\times\tfrac{1}{2}\right)+\left(\tfrac{1}{2}\times\tfrac{1}{2}\right)+\left(\tfrac{1}{2}\times\tfrac{1}{2}\right)+\left(1\times\tfrac{1}{2}\right)$$
$$=\tfrac{3}{2}$$

(b) $L(f,P)=\sum_{i=1}^{3}m_i\,\delta x_i$
$$=\left(\tfrac{1}{4}\times\tfrac{3}{4}\right)+\left(0\times\tfrac{7}{12}\right)+\left(\tfrac{1}{3}\times\tfrac{2}{3}\right)=\tfrac{59}{144}$$

$U(f,P)=\sum_{i=1}^{3}M_i\,\delta x_i$
$$=\left(1\times\tfrac{3}{4}\right)+\left(\tfrac{1}{3}\times\tfrac{7}{12}\right)+\left(1\times\tfrac{2}{3}\right)=\tfrac{29}{18}$$

1.5

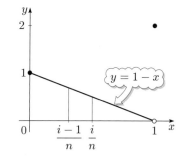

(a) We have

$$P_n = \left\{ \left[0, \frac{1}{n}\right], \left[\frac{1}{n}, \frac{2}{n}\right], \ldots, \left[\frac{n-1}{n}, 1\right] \right\}.$$

On $\left[\dfrac{i-1}{n}, \dfrac{i}{n}\right]$, for $i = 1, 2, \ldots, n-1$, we have

$$m_i = f\left(\frac{i}{n}\right) = 1 - \frac{i}{n},$$

$$M_i = f\left(\frac{i-1}{n}\right) = 1 - \frac{i-1}{n}.$$

Also, $m_n = 0$, $M_n = f(1) = 2$, and

$$\delta x_i = \frac{1}{n}, \quad \text{for } i = 1, 2, \ldots, n.$$

Hence

$$
\begin{aligned}
L(f, P_n) &= \sum_{i=1}^{n} m_i\, \delta x_i \\
&= \sum_{i=1}^{n} f\left(\frac{i}{n}\right)\frac{1}{n} \\
&= \frac{1}{n}\sum_{i=1}^{n}\left(1 - \frac{i}{n}\right) \\
&= \frac{1}{n} \times n - \frac{1}{n^2}\sum_{i=1}^{n} i \\
&= 1 - \frac{1}{n^2} \times \frac{n(n+1)}{2} \\
&= \frac{1}{2} - \frac{1}{2n} \to \frac{1}{2} \quad \text{as } n \to \infty,
\end{aligned}
$$

$$
\begin{aligned}
U(f, P_n) &= \sum_{i=1}^{n} M_i\, \delta x_i \\
&= \sum_{i=1}^{n-1} f\left(\frac{i-1}{n}\right)\frac{1}{n} + \left(2 \times \frac{1}{n}\right) \\
&= \frac{1}{n}\sum_{i=1}^{n-1}\left(1 - \frac{i-1}{n}\right) + \frac{2}{n} \\
&= \frac{1}{n}\sum_{i=1}^{n-1}\left(1 + \frac{1}{n} - \frac{i}{n}\right) + \frac{2}{n} \\
&= \frac{n-1}{n}\left(1 + \frac{1}{n}\right) - \frac{1}{n^2}\sum_{i=1}^{n-1} i + \frac{2}{n} \\
&= \frac{n^2-1}{n^2} - \frac{1}{n^2} \times \frac{(n-1)n}{2} + \frac{2}{n} \\
&= \frac{1}{2} - \frac{1}{n^2} + \frac{5}{2n} \to \frac{1}{2} \quad \text{as } n \to \infty.
\end{aligned}
$$

(b) Since $\|P_n\| \to 0$ as $n \to \infty$, and

$$\lim_{n \to \infty} L(f, P_n) = \lim_{n \to \infty} U(f, P_n) = \tfrac{1}{2},$$

it follows from Theorem 1.3 that f is integrable on $[0, 1]$ and

$$\int_0^1 f = \tfrac{1}{2}.$$

1.6 The standard partition P_n of $[a, b]$ consists of n intervals $[x_{i-1}, x_i]$, $i = 1, 2, \ldots, n$, each of length $\delta x_i = (b-a)/n$. Also,

$$m_i = M_i = c, \quad \text{for } i = 1, 2, \ldots, n.$$

Thus

$$L(f, P_n) = \sum_{i=1}^{n} m_i\, \delta x_i = \sum_{i=1}^{n} c\,\frac{b-a}{n} = c(b-a),$$

$$U(f, P_n) = \sum_{i=1}^{n} M_i\, \delta x_i = \sum_{i=1}^{n} c\,\frac{b-a}{n} = c(b-a).$$

Since $\|P_n\| \to 0$ as $n \to \infty$, and

$$\lim_{n \to \infty} L(f, P_n) = \lim_{n \to \infty} U(f, P_n) = c(b-a),$$

it follows from Theorem 1.3 that f is integrable on $[a, b]$ and

$$\int_a^b f = c(b-a).$$

1.7

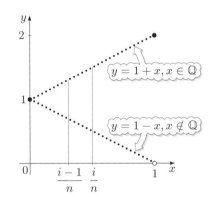

Let P_n be the standard partition of $[0, 1]$:

$$\left\{ \left[0, \frac{1}{n}\right], \left[\frac{1}{n}, \frac{2}{n}\right], \ldots, \left[\frac{n-1}{n}, 1\right] \right\}.$$

Each subinterval

$$\left[\frac{i-1}{n}, \frac{i}{n}\right], \quad \text{for } i = 1, 2, \ldots, n,$$

contains both rational and irrational points:

at the rational points, $f(x) = 1 + x \geq 1$,
at the irrational points, $f(x) = 1 - x \leq 1$.

Hence

$$m_i = 1 - \frac{i}{n} \quad \text{and} \quad M_i = 1 + \frac{i}{n}.$$

Also,

$$\delta x_i = \frac{1}{n}, \quad \text{for } i = 1, 2, \ldots, n.$$

Hence

$$L(f, P_n) = \sum_{i=1}^{n} m_i \, \delta x_i$$

$$= \frac{1}{n} \sum_{i=1}^{n} \left(1 - \frac{i}{n}\right)$$

$$= \frac{1}{n} \times n - \frac{1}{n^2} \sum_{i=1}^{n} i$$

$$= 1 - \frac{1}{n^2} \times \frac{n(n+1)}{2}$$

$$= \frac{1}{2} - \frac{1}{2n},$$

$$U(f, P_n) = \sum_{i=1}^{n} M_i \, \delta x_i$$

$$= \frac{1}{n} \sum_{i=1}^{n} \left(1 + \frac{i}{n}\right)$$

$$= \frac{1}{n} \times n + \frac{1}{n^2} \sum_{i=1}^{n} i$$

$$= 1 + \frac{1}{n^2} \times \frac{n(n+1)}{2}$$

$$= \frac{3}{2} + \frac{1}{2n}.$$

Now $\|P_n\| \to 0$ as $n \to \infty$, and

$$\lim_{n \to \infty} L(f, P_n) = \tfrac{1}{2} \neq \tfrac{3}{2} = \lim_{n \to \infty} U(f, P_n).$$

Thus f is not integrable on $[0, 1]$, by Theorem 1.2.

1.8 Since f and g are integrable on $[a, b]$, so is $f - g$, by the Sum and Multiple Rules, and so therefore is $|f - g|$, by the Modulus Rule.

Hence the function

$$\max\{f, g\} = \tfrac{1}{2}\left(f + g + |f - g|\right)$$

is integrable on $[a, b]$, by the Sum and Multiple Rules.

2.1 (a) We have

$$F'(x) = \frac{1}{x + (x^2 - 4)^{1/2}} \left(1 + \tfrac{1}{2}(x^2 - 4)^{-1/2} \, 2x\right)$$

$$= \frac{(x^2 - 4)^{-1/2} \left((x^2 - 4)^{1/2} + x\right)}{x + (x^2 - 4)^{1/2}}$$

$$= (x^2 - 4)^{-1/2} = f(x),$$

as required.

(b) We have

$$F'(x) = \frac{1}{1 + \sinh^2 x} \cosh x$$

$$= \frac{\cosh x}{\cosh^2 x}$$

$$= \operatorname{sech} x = f(x),$$

as required.

2.2 (a) From the Fundamental Theorem of Calculus and the table of standard primitives, we deduce that

$$\int_0^4 (x^2 + 9)^{1/2} \, dx$$

$$= \left[\tfrac{1}{2}x(x^2 + 9)^{1/2} + \tfrac{9}{2}\log_e\left(x + (x^2 + 9)^{1/2}\right)\right]_0^4$$

$$= 10 + \tfrac{9}{2}\log_e 9 - \tfrac{9}{2}\log_e 3$$

$$= 10 + \tfrac{9}{2}\log_e 3.$$

(b) From the Fundamental Theorem of Calculus and the table of standard primitives, we deduce that

$$\int_1^e \log_e x \, dx = \left[x \log_e x - x\right]_1^e$$

$$= (e - e) - (0 - 1) = 1.$$

2.3 Using the table of standard primitives and the Combination Rules, we obtain the following primitives.

(a) $F(x) = 4(x \log_e x - x) - \tan^{-1}(x/2)$

(b) $F(x) = \tfrac{2}{3}\log_e(\sec 3x) + \tfrac{1}{5}e^{2x}(2\cos x + \sin x)$

(These results can be checked by differentiation.)

2.4 (a) Take $u = \sin 3x$; then

$$\frac{du}{dx} = 3\cos 3x, \quad \text{so} \quad du = 3\cos 3x \, dx.$$

Hence

$$\int \sin(\sin 3x) \cos 3x \, dx = \tfrac{1}{3} \int \sin u \, du$$

$$= -\tfrac{1}{3}\cos u$$

$$= -\tfrac{1}{3}\cos(\sin 3x).$$

(b) Taking $u = 2 + 3x^3$, we obtain

$$\int x^2 (2 + 3x^3)^7 \, dx = \tfrac{1}{72}(2 + 3x^3)^8.$$

(c) Taking $u = 2x^2$, we obtain

$$\int x \sin(2x^2) \, dx = -\tfrac{1}{4}\cos(2x^2).$$

(d) Using equation (2.4), we obtain

$$\int x/(2 + 3x^2) \, dx = \tfrac{1}{6}\log_e(2 + 3x^2).$$

2.5 Let $u = e^x$; then

$$\frac{du}{dx} = e^x, \quad \text{so} \quad du = e^x \, dx.$$

Also,

when $x = 0, \quad u = 1,$

when $x = 1, \quad u = e.$

Hence

$$\int_0^1 \frac{e^x}{(1 + e^x)^2} \, dx = \int_1^e \frac{du}{(1 + u)^2}$$

$$= \left[\frac{-1}{1 + u}\right]_1^e$$

$$= -\frac{1}{1 + e} + \frac{1}{2} = \frac{e - 1}{2(1 + e)}.$$

2.6 (a) Let $u = (x-1)^{1/2}$, so $x = u^2 + 1$; then
$$\frac{dx}{du} = 2u, \quad \text{so} \quad dx = 2u\,du.$$
Hence
$$\int \frac{dx}{3(x-1)^{3/2} + x(x-1)^{1/2}}$$
$$= \int \frac{2u}{3u^3 + (u^2+1)u}\,du$$
$$= \int \frac{2}{4u^2 + 1}\,du$$
$$= \tan^{-1}(2u) = \tan^{-1}(2(x-1)^{1/2}).$$

(b) Let $u = \sqrt{1 + e^x}$, so $x = \log_e(u^2 - 1)$; then
$$\frac{dx}{du} = \frac{2u}{u^2 - 1}, \quad \text{so} \quad dx = \frac{2u}{u^2 - 1}\,du.$$
Also,
$$\text{when } x = 0, \qquad u = \sqrt{2},$$
$$\text{when } x = \log_e 3, \quad u = 2.$$
Hence
$$\int_0^{\log_e 3} e^x \sqrt{1 + e^x}\,dx = \int_{\sqrt{2}}^2 (u^2 - 1)u\frac{2u}{u^2 - 1}\,du$$
$$= \int_{\sqrt{2}}^2 2u^2\,du$$
$$= \left[\tfrac{2}{3}u^3\right]_{\sqrt{2}}^2$$
$$= (16 - 4\sqrt{2})/3.$$

2.7 (a) Here we use integration by parts, with
$$f(x) = \log_e x \quad \text{and} \quad g'(x) = x^{1/3};$$
then
$$f'(x) = 1/x \quad \text{and} \quad g(x) = \tfrac{3}{4}x^{4/3}.$$
Hence
$$\int x^{1/3} \log_e x\,dx = \tfrac{3}{4}x^{4/3} \log_e x - \tfrac{3}{4}\int x^{4/3}x^{-1}\,dx$$
$$= \tfrac{3}{4}x^{4/3} \log_e x - \tfrac{3}{4}\int x^{1/3}\,dx$$
$$= \tfrac{3}{4}x^{4/3} \log_e x - \tfrac{9}{16}x^{4/3}.$$

(b) We use integration by parts twice. On each occasion we differentiate the power function and integrate the trigonometric function.
We have
$$\int_0^{\pi/2} x^2 \cos x\,dx = \left[x^2 \sin x\right]_0^{\pi/2} - \int_0^{\pi/2} 2x \sin x\,dx$$
$$= \frac{\pi^2}{4} - 2\int_0^{\pi/2} x \sin x\,dx$$
and
$$\int_0^{\pi/2} x \sin x\,dx = \left[x(-\cos x)\right]_0^{\pi/2} - \int_0^{\pi/2} (-\cos x)\,dx$$
$$= 0 + \left[\sin x\right]_0^{\pi/2} = 1.$$
It follows that
$$\int_0^{\pi/2} x^2 \cos x\,dx = \frac{\pi^2}{4} - 2.$$

2.8 (a) $I_0 = \displaystyle\int_0^1 e^x\,dx = [e^x]_0^1 = e - 1.$

(b) Using integration by parts, we obtain
$$I_n = \int_0^1 e^x x^n\,dx$$
$$= [e^x x^n]_0^1 - \int_0^1 e^x n x^{n-1}\,dx$$
$$= e - nI_{n-1}, \quad \text{for } n \geq 1.$$

(c) Using the solution to part (b) with $n = 1, 2, 3, 4$ in turn, we obtain
$$I_1 = e - I_0 = e - (e - 1) = 1,$$
$$I_2 = e - 2I_1 = e - 2,$$
$$I_3 = e - 3I_2 = e - 3(e - 2) = 6 - 2e,$$
$$I_4 = e - 4I_3 = e - 4(6 - 2e) = 9e - 24.$$

2.9 Using the table of standard primitives and the Combination Rules, we obtain the following primitives.

(a) $F(x) = \tfrac{1}{2}x(x^2 - 9)^{1/2} - \tfrac{9}{2}\log_e(x + (x^2 - 9)^{1/2})$

(b) $F(x) = -\tfrac{1}{2}\cos(2x + 3) - \tfrac{4}{3}\sin(3x - 2)$

(c) $F(x) = \tfrac{1}{13}e^{2x}(2\sin 3x - 3\cos 3x)$

2.10 Since all primitives of f differ only by a constant, by Theorem 2.2, we take
$$F(x) = c + \tfrac{1}{13}e^{2x}(2\sin 3x - 3\cos 3x)$$
and choose a value of c such that $F(\pi) = 0$. Thus
$$0 = F(\pi) = c + \tfrac{1}{13}e^{2\pi}(2\sin 3\pi - 3\cos 3\pi),$$
so
$$c = -\tfrac{3}{13}e^{2\pi}.$$

2.11 (a) Let $u = \sin x$; then
$$\frac{du}{dx} = \cos x, \quad \text{so} \quad du = \cos x\,dx.$$
Also,
$$\text{when } x = 0, \qquad u = 0,$$
$$\text{when } x = \pi/2, \quad u = 1.$$
Hence
$$\int_0^{\pi/2} \tan(\sin x) \cos x\,dx = \int_0^1 \tan u\,du$$
$$= [\log_e(\sec u)]_0^1$$
$$= \log_e(\sec 1) - \log_e 1$$
$$= \log_e(\sec 1).$$

(b) Let $u = \tan^{-1} x$, so $x = \tan u$; then
$$\frac{dx}{du} = \sec^2 u, \quad \text{so} \quad dx = \sec^2 u\,du.$$
Also,
$$\text{when } x = 0, \quad u = 0,$$
$$\text{when } x = 1, \quad u = \pi/4.$$

Hence
$$\int_0^1 \frac{(\tan^{-1} x)^2}{1 + x^2}\, dx$$
$$= \int_0^{\pi/4} \frac{u^2 \sec^2 u}{1 + \tan^2 u}\, du$$
$$= \int_0^{\pi/4} u^2\, du \quad (\text{since } 1 + \tan^2 u = \sec^2 u)$$
$$= \left[\tfrac{1}{3} u^3\right]_0^{\pi/4} = \pi^3/192.$$

(c) Since
$$\frac{\sin 2x}{1 + 3\cos^2 x} = \frac{2\sin x \cos x}{1 + 3\cos^2 x}$$
and
$$g'(x) = -6\cos x \sin x, \quad \text{where } g(x) = 1 + 3\cos^2 x,$$
the integral is of the form $-\tfrac{1}{3}\int g'(x)/g(x)\, dx$. Thus, by equation (2.4),
$$\int_0^{\pi/2} \frac{\sin 2x}{1 + 3\cos^2 x}\, dx = \left[-\tfrac{1}{3}\log_e(1 + 3\cos^2 x)\right]_0^{\pi/2}$$
$$= -\tfrac{1}{3}\log_e 1 + \tfrac{1}{3}\log_e 4$$
$$= \tfrac{2}{3}\log_e 2.$$

(d) Here we use integration by parts, with
$$f(x) = \log_e x \quad \text{and} \quad g'(x) = 8x^7;$$
then
$$f'(x) = 1/x \quad \text{and} \quad g(x) = x^8.$$
Hence
$$\int_1^e 8x^7 \log_e x\, dx = \left[x^8 \log_e x\right]_1^e - \int_1^e x^8 \frac{1}{x}\, dx$$
$$= e^8 - \int_1^e x^7\, dx$$
$$= e^8 - \left[\tfrac{1}{8} x^8\right]_1^e$$
$$= e^8 - \tfrac{1}{8} e^8 + \tfrac{1}{8} = \tfrac{1}{8}(7e^8 + 1).$$

(e) Here we use integration by parts, with
$$f(x) = \log_e(\log_e x) \quad \text{and} \quad g'(x) = \frac{1}{x};$$
then
$$f'(x) = \frac{1}{\log_e x} \times \frac{1}{x} \quad \text{and} \quad g(x) = \log_e x.$$
Hence
$$\int_e^{e^2} \frac{\log_e(\log_e x)}{x}\, dx$$
$$= \left[\log_e(\log_e x) \log_e x\right]_e^{e^2} - \int_e^{e^2} \frac{\log_e x}{x \log_e x}\, dx$$
$$= 2\log_e 2 - \log_e 1 - \left[\log_e x\right]_e^{e^2}$$
$$= 2\log_e 2 - (2 - 1) = 2\log_e 2 - 1.$$

(f) Let $u = \sqrt{x}$, so $x = u^2$; then
$$\frac{dx}{du} = 2u, \quad \text{so} \quad dx = 2u\, du.$$
Also,
when $x = 1$, $\quad u = 1$,
when $x = 4$, $\quad u = 2$.

Hence
$$\int_1^4 \frac{dx}{(1 + x)\sqrt{x}} = \int_1^2 \frac{2u}{(1 + u^2)u}\, du$$
$$= \left[2\tan^{-1} u\right]_1^2$$
$$= 2\tan^{-1} 2 - \pi/2.$$

(g) Let $u = \tan(\tfrac{1}{2}x)$; then
$$\frac{du}{dx} = \tfrac{1}{2}\sec^2(\tfrac{1}{2}x), \quad \text{so} \quad dx = \frac{2}{1 + u^2}\, du,$$
since $\sec^2(\tfrac{1}{2}x) = 1 + \tan^2(\tfrac{1}{2}x)$. Also,
when $x = 0$, $\quad u = 0$,
when $x = \pi/2$, $\quad u = 1$.

Next, by the given identity,
$$\cos x = \frac{1 - \tan^2(\tfrac{1}{2}x)}{1 + \tan^2(\tfrac{1}{2}x)} = \frac{1 - u^2}{1 + u^2},$$
so
$$\frac{1}{2 + \cos x} = \frac{1}{2 + (1 - u^2)/(1 + u^2)} = \frac{1 + u^2}{3 + u^2}.$$
Hence
$$\int_0^{\pi/2} \frac{dx}{2 + \cos x} = \int_0^1 \frac{1 + u^2}{3 + u^2} \frac{2}{1 + u^2}\, du$$
$$= 2\int_0^1 \frac{du}{3 + u^2}$$
$$= \frac{2}{\sqrt{3}} \left[\tan^{-1}(u/\sqrt{3})\right]_0^1$$
$$= \frac{2}{\sqrt{3}} \times \frac{\pi}{6} = \frac{\sqrt{3}\,\pi}{9}.$$

2.12 (a) Here we use integration by parts, with
$$f(x) = (\log_e x)^n \quad \text{and} \quad g'(x) = x;$$
then
$$f'(x) = n(\log_e x)^{n-1} x^{-1} \quad \text{and} \quad g(x) = \tfrac{1}{2} x^2.$$
Hence
$$I_n = \left[\tfrac{1}{2} x^2 (\log_e x)^n\right]_1^e - \int_1^e \tfrac{1}{2} x^2 n(\log_e x)^{n-1} x^{-1}\, dx$$
$$= \tfrac{1}{2} e^2 - \tfrac{1}{2} n \int_1^e x(\log_e x)^{n-1}\, dx$$
$$= \tfrac{1}{2} e^2 - \tfrac{1}{2} n I_{n-1}, \quad \text{for } n \geq 1.$$

(b) First,
$$I_0 = \int_1^e x\, dx$$
$$= \left[\tfrac{1}{2} x^2\right]_1^e = \tfrac{1}{2} e^2 - \tfrac{1}{2}.$$
Using the formula from part (a), we obtain
$$I_1 = \tfrac{1}{2} e^2 - \tfrac{1}{2} I_0$$
$$= \tfrac{1}{2} e^2 - \tfrac{1}{2}\left(\tfrac{1}{2} e^2 - \tfrac{1}{2}\right) = \tfrac{1}{4} e^2 + \tfrac{1}{4},$$
$$I_2 = \tfrac{1}{2} e^2 - \tfrac{1}{2} \times 2 \times I_1$$
$$= \tfrac{1}{2} e^2 - \left(\tfrac{1}{4} e^2 + \tfrac{1}{4}\right) = \tfrac{1}{4} e^2 - \tfrac{1}{4},$$
$$I_3 = \tfrac{1}{2} e^2 - \tfrac{1}{2} \times 3 \times I_2$$
$$= \tfrac{1}{2} e^2 - \tfrac{3}{2}\left(\tfrac{1}{4} e^2 - \tfrac{1}{4}\right) = \tfrac{1}{8} e^2 + \tfrac{3}{8}.$$

3.1 **(a)** Since $\sin(1/x^{10}) \leq 1$, we have
$$x \sin(1/x^{10}) \leq x, \quad \text{for } x \in [1,3].$$
It follows from Inequality Rule(a) that
$$\int_1^3 x \sin(1/x^{10})\, dx \leq \int_1^3 x\, dx$$
$$= \left[\tfrac{1}{2}x^2\right]_1^3$$
$$= \tfrac{1}{2}(9-1) = 4.$$

(b) If $x \in [0, \tfrac{1}{2}]$, then
$$1 = e^0 \leq e^{x^2} \leq e^{(1/2)^2} = e^{1/4},$$
because the function $x \longmapsto e^{x^2}$ is increasing on $[0, \tfrac{1}{2}]$.
It follows from Inequality Rule(b) that
$$\tfrac{1}{2} \leq \int_0^{1/2} e^{x^2}\, dx \leq \tfrac{1}{2}e^{1/4}.$$

3.2 **(a)** Since
$$|\sin(1/x)| \leq 1, \quad \text{for } x \in [1,4],$$
and
$$2 + \cos(1/x) \geq 1, \quad \text{for } x \in [1,4],$$
it follows that
$$\left|\frac{\sin(1/x)}{2 + \cos(1/x)}\right| \leq 1, \quad \text{for } x \in [1,4].$$
Hence, by the Triangle Inequality,
$$\left|\int_1^4 \frac{\sin(1/x)}{2 + \cos(1/x)}\, dx\right| \leq 1(4-1) = 3.$$

(b) Since
$$\tan x \geq 0, \quad \text{for } x \in [0, \pi/4],$$
and
$$3 - \sin(x^2) \geq 2, \quad \text{for } x \in [0, \pi/4],$$
it follows that
$$0 \leq \frac{\tan x}{3 - \sin(x^2)} \leq \tfrac{1}{2}\tan x, \quad \text{for } x \in [0, \pi/4].$$
Hence, by the Triangle Inequality and Inequality Rule(a),
$$\left|\int_0^{\pi/4} \frac{\tan x}{3 - \sin(x^2)}\, dx\right| \leq \int_0^{\pi/4} \left|\frac{\tan x}{3 - \sin(x^2)}\right|\, dx$$
$$\leq \int_0^{\pi/4} \tfrac{1}{2}\tan x\, dx$$
$$= \left[\tfrac{1}{2}\log_e(\sec x)\right]_0^{\pi/4}$$
$$= \tfrac{1}{2}(\log_e(\sec \pi/4) - \log_e 1)$$
$$= \tfrac{1}{2}\log_e(\sqrt{2}) = \tfrac{1}{4}\log_e 2.$$

3.3 **(a)** We have
$$a_1 = \frac{2}{1} \cdot \frac{2}{3} = \frac{4}{3},$$
$$a_2 = \frac{2}{1} \cdot \frac{2}{3} \cdot \frac{4}{3} \cdot \frac{4}{5} = \frac{64}{45},$$
$$a_3 = \frac{2}{1} \cdot \frac{2}{3} \cdot \frac{4}{3} \cdot \frac{4}{5} \cdot \frac{6}{5} \cdot \frac{6}{7} = \frac{256}{175},$$
$$b_1 = \frac{(1!)^2\, 2^2}{2!\sqrt{1}} = 2,$$
$$b_2 = \frac{(2!)^2\, 2^4}{4!\sqrt{2}} = \frac{4}{3}\sqrt{2},$$
$$b_3 = \frac{(3!)^2\, 2^6}{6!\sqrt{3}} = \frac{16}{15}\sqrt{3}.$$

(b) Using the results of part (a),
$$b_1^2 = 4 = 3a_1,$$
$$b_2^2 = \frac{32}{9} = \frac{5}{2}a_2,$$
$$b_3^2 = \frac{256}{75} = \frac{7}{3}a_3,$$
as required.

(c) We have
$$b_n^2 = \frac{(n!)^4\, 2^{4n}}{((2n)!)^2\, n}.$$
We now try to express
$$a_n = \frac{2 \cdot 2 \cdot 4 \cdot 4 \cdot \cdots \cdot (2n)(2n)}{1 \cdot 3 \cdot 3 \cdot 5 \cdot \cdots \cdot (2n-1)(2n+1)}$$
in terms of factorials.

The numerator is a product of $2n$ even numbers.
Taking a factor 2 from each term, we deduce that
$$2 \cdot 2 \cdot 4 \cdot 4 \cdot \cdots \cdot (2n)(2n)$$
$$= 2^{2n}(1 \cdot 1 \cdot 2 \cdot 2 \cdot \cdots \cdot n \cdot n) = 2^{2n}(n!)^2.$$

The denominator of a_n cannot be treated in quite the same way, as all its factors are odd. To relate it to factorials, we introduce the missing even factors:
$$1 \cdot 3 \cdot 3 \cdot 5 \cdot 5 \cdot \cdots \cdot (2n-1)(2n+1)$$
$$= \frac{1 \cdot 2 \cdot 2 \cdot 3 \cdot 3 \cdot 4 \cdot 4 \cdot \cdots \cdot (2n-1)(2n)(2n)(2n+1)}{2 \cdot 2 \cdot 4 \cdot 4 \cdot \cdots \cdot (2n)(2n)}$$
$$= \frac{((2n)!)^2\, (2n+1)}{2^{2n}(n!)^2}.$$
It follows that
$$a_n = 2^{2n}(n!)^2 \Big/ \frac{((2n)!)^2\, (2n+1)}{2^{2n}(n!)^2}$$
$$= \frac{2^{4n}(n!)^4}{((2n)!)^2(2n+1)}$$
$$= b_n^2 \left(\frac{n}{2n+1}\right).$$
Hence
$$b_n^2 = \left(\frac{2n+1}{n}\right) a_n,$$
as required.

3.4 (a) Let

$$f(x) = \frac{1}{x} \quad (x \in [1, \infty)).$$

Then f is positive and decreasing on $[1, \infty)$, and

$$f(x) \to 0 \quad \text{as } x \to \infty.$$

Also, for $n \geq 1$,

$$\int_1^n f = \int_1^n \frac{dx}{x}$$
$$= \left[\log_e x \right]_1^n$$
$$= \log_e n \to \infty \quad \text{as } n \to \infty.$$

Hence, by the Integral Test, the series diverges.

(b) Let $u = \log_e x$; then

$$\frac{du}{dx} = \frac{1}{x}, \quad \text{so} \quad du = \frac{dx}{x}.$$

Hence

$$\int \frac{dx}{x(\log_e x)^2} = \int \frac{du}{u^2} = -\frac{1}{u} = -\frac{1}{\log_e x}.$$

Let

$$f(x) = \frac{1}{x(\log_e x)^2} \quad (x \in [2, \infty)).$$

Then f is positive and decreasing on $[2, \infty)$, and

$$f(x) \to 0 \quad \text{as } x \to \infty.$$

Also, for $n \geq 2$,

$$\int_2^n f = \int_2^n \frac{dx}{x(\log_e x)^2}$$
$$= \left[-\frac{1}{\log_e x} \right]_2^n$$
$$= \frac{1}{\log_e 2} - \frac{1}{\log_e n} \leq \frac{1}{\log_e 2}.$$

Since the sequence $\left\{ \int_2^n f \right\}_2^\infty$ is bounded above, it follows from the Integral Test that the series converges.

3.5 (a) If $x \in [0, 1]$, then

$$x^3 \sqrt{2(1 + x^{99})} \leq x^3 \sqrt{2(1 + 1)} = 2x^3.$$

Hence, by Inequality Rule(a),

$$\int_0^1 x^3 \sqrt{2(1 + x^{99})}\, dx \leq \int_0^1 2x^3\, dx$$
$$= \left[\tfrac{1}{2} x^4 \right]_0^1 = \tfrac{1}{2}.$$

(b) If $x \in [0, 1]$, then

$$1 + 3x^{97} \leq 1 + 3 = 4,$$

so

$$\frac{x^4}{(1 + 3x^{97})^{1/2}} \geq \frac{x^4}{4^{1/2}} = \tfrac{1}{2} x^4.$$

Hence, by Inequality Rule(a),

$$\int_0^1 \frac{x^4}{(1 + 3x^{97})^{1/2}}\, dx \geq \int_0^1 \tfrac{1}{2} x^4\, dx$$
$$= \left[\tfrac{1}{10} x^5 \right]_0^1 = \tfrac{1}{10}.$$

3.6 (a) If $x \in [0, 1]$, then

$$1 \leq 1 + x^{30} \leq 1 + 1 = 2$$

and

$$1 \leq 2 - x^{99} \leq 2,$$

so

$$\tfrac{1}{2} \leq \frac{1}{2 - x^{99}} \leq 1.$$

Hence

$$\tfrac{1}{2} \leq \frac{1 + x^{30}}{2 - x^{99}} \leq 2, \quad \text{for } x \in [0, 1].$$

Since the length of $[0, 1]$ is 1, it follows, by Inequality Rule(b), that

$$\tfrac{1}{2} \leq \int_0^1 \frac{1 + x^{30}}{2 - x^{99}}\, dx \leq 2.$$

(b) If $x \in [0, 2]$, then $1 + x^{20} \geq 1$ and $|\sin 9x| \leq 1$, so

$$\left| \frac{x^2(x - 3)\sin 9x}{1 + x^{20}} \right| \leq x^2 |x - 3|$$
$$= x^2(3 - x)$$
$$= 3x^2 - x^3.$$

Hence, by the Triangle Inequality and Inequality Rule(a),

$$\left| \int_0^2 \frac{x^2(x - 3)\sin 9x}{1 + x^{20}}\, dx \right| \leq \int_0^2 \left| \frac{x^2(x - 3)\sin 9x}{1 + x^{20}} \right|\, dx$$
$$\leq \int_0^2 (3x^2 - x^3)\, dx$$
$$= \left[x^3 - \tfrac{1}{4} x^4 \right]_0^2$$
$$= 8 - 4 = 4.$$

3.7 (a) Let $u = \log_e x$; then

$$\frac{du}{dx} = \frac{1}{x}, \quad \text{so} \quad du = \frac{dx}{x}.$$

Hence

$$\int \frac{dx}{x(\log_e x)^{3/2}} = \int \frac{du}{u^{3/2}} = -\frac{2}{u^{1/2}} = -\frac{2}{(\log_e x)^{1/2}}.$$

Let

$$f(x) = \frac{1}{x(\log_e x)^{3/2}} \quad (x \in [2, \infty)).$$

Then f is positive and decreasing on $[2, \infty)$, and

$$f(x) \to 0 \quad \text{as } x \to \infty.$$

Also, for $n \geq 2$,

$$\int_2^n f = \int_2^n \frac{dx}{x(\log_e x)^{3/2}}$$
$$= \left[\frac{-2}{(\log_e x)^{1/2}} \right]_2^n$$
$$= 2 \left(\frac{1}{(\log_e 2)^{1/2}} - \frac{1}{(\log_e n)^{1/2}} \right) \leq \frac{2}{(\log_e 2)^{1/2}}.$$

Since the sequence $\left\{ \int_2^n f \right\}$ is bounded above, it follows from the Integral Test that the series converges.

(b) Let $u = \log_e x$, as in part (a). Then

$$\int \frac{dx}{x \log_e x} = \int \frac{du}{u} = \log_e u = \log_e(\log_e x).$$

Let

$$f(x) = \frac{1}{x \log_e x} \quad (x \in [2, \infty)).$$

Then f is positive and decreasing on $[2, \infty)$, and

$$f(x) \to 0 \quad \text{as } x \to \infty.$$

Also, for $n \geq 2$,

$$\int_2^n f = \int_2^n \frac{dx}{x \log_e x}$$
$$= \left[\log_e(\log_e x) \right]_2^n$$
$$= \log_e(\log_e n) - \log_e(\log_e 2) \to \infty \quad \text{as } n \to \infty.$$

Hence, by the Integral Test, the series diverges.

4.1 The values are as follows.

n	$n!$
30	$2.652\ldots \times 10^{32}$
40	$8.159\ldots \times 10^{47}$
50	$3.041\ldots \times 10^{64}$
60	$8.320\ldots \times 10^{81}$

4.2 The values are as follows.

n	$\sqrt{2\pi n}\,(n/e)^n$
5	$118.019\ldots$
10	$3.598\ldots \times 10^6$
50	$3.036\ldots \times 10^{64}$

4.3 In each part we approximate the factorials using Stirling's formula.

(a) $\displaystyle \binom{300}{150} \frac{1}{2^{300}} = \frac{300!}{150!\,150!\,2^{300}}$

$$\simeq \frac{\sqrt{600\pi}\,(300/e)^{300}}{\left(\sqrt{300\pi}\,(150/e)^{150}\right)^2 2^{300}}$$
$$= \frac{\sqrt{600\pi}}{300\pi}$$
$$= \frac{\sqrt{6}}{30\sqrt{\pi}} = 0.046 \quad \text{(to 2 s.f.).}$$

(b) $\displaystyle \frac{300!}{(100!)^3} \frac{1}{3^{300}} \simeq \frac{\sqrt{600\pi}\,(300/e)^{300}}{(200\pi)^{3/2}\,(100/e)^{300}\,3^{300}}$

$$= \frac{\sqrt{600\pi}}{(200\pi)^{3/2}}$$
$$= \frac{\sqrt{3}}{200\pi} = 0.0028 \quad \text{(to 2 s.f.).}$$

4.4 We have

$$\binom{4n}{2n} = \frac{(4n)!}{((2n)!)^2} \quad \text{and} \quad \binom{2n}{n} = \frac{(2n)!}{(n!)^2},$$

so

$$\binom{4n}{2n} \Big/ \binom{2n}{n} = \frac{(4n)!\,(n!)^2}{((2n)!)^3}.$$

By Stirling's Formula, and the Product and Quotient Rules for $\sim$, we obtain

$$\binom{4n}{2n} \Big/ \binom{2n}{n} \sim \frac{\sqrt{8\pi n}\,(4n/e)^{4n}\,\left(\sqrt{2\pi n}\,(n/e)^n\right)^2}{\left(\sqrt{4\pi n}\,(2n/e)^{2n}\right)^3}$$

$$= \frac{\sqrt{8\pi n}\,4^{4n}\,2\pi n}{(4\pi n)^{3/2}\,2^{6n}}$$

$$= \frac{2\sqrt{8}}{8}\frac{4^{4n}}{2^{6n}} = \frac{1}{\sqrt{2}}\,2^{2n}.$$

Hence $\lambda = 1/\sqrt{2}$.

4.5 Using Stirling's Formula, we obtain

$$\frac{n^n}{n!} \sim \frac{n^n}{\sqrt{2\pi n}\,(n/e)^n} = \frac{e^n}{\sqrt{2\pi n}}.$$

Thus, by the hint,

$$\left(\frac{n^n}{n!}\right)^{1/n} \sim \left(\frac{e^n}{\sqrt{2\pi n}}\right)^{1/n} = \frac{e}{\left(\sqrt{2\pi}\right)^{1/n}\sqrt{n^{1/n}}}.$$

We know (from Unit AA2, Example 3.2 and Exercise 3.4) that, for any positive number a,

$$a^{1/n} \to 1 \quad \text{as } n \to \infty$$

and

$$n^{1/n} \to 1 \quad \text{as } n \to \infty.$$

Hence

$$\left(\sqrt{2\pi}\right)^{1/n} \to 1 \quad \text{as } n \to \infty$$

and

$$\sqrt{n^{1/n}} \to 1 \quad \text{as } n \to \infty.$$

It follows that

$$\left(\frac{n^n}{n!}\right)^{1/n} \sim e \quad \text{as } n \to \infty;$$

that is,

$$\left(\frac{n^n}{n!}\right)^{1/n} \to e \quad \text{as } n \to \infty.$$

4.6 In each part we approximate the factorials using Stirling's formula.

(a) $\displaystyle \binom{400}{200}\left(\frac{1}{2}\right)^{400} = \frac{400!}{200!\,200!\,2^{400}}$

$$\simeq \frac{\sqrt{800\pi}\,(400/e)^{400}}{\left(\sqrt{400\pi}\,(200/e)^{200}\right)^2 2^{400}}$$
$$= \frac{\sqrt{800\pi}}{400\pi}$$
$$= \frac{\sqrt{8}}{40\sqrt{\pi}} = 0.040 \quad \text{(to 2 s.f.).}$$

(b) $\dfrac{400!\,\sqrt{800\pi}}{(100!)^4\,4^{400}} \simeq \dfrac{\sqrt{800\pi}\,(400/e)^{400}\,\sqrt{800\pi}}{\left(\sqrt{200\pi}\,(100/e)^{100}\right)^4\,4^{400}}$

$$= \dfrac{800\pi}{(\sqrt{200\pi}\,)^4}$$

$$= \dfrac{1}{50\pi} = 0.0064 \quad \text{(to 2 s.f.)}.$$

4.7 By Stirling's Formula, and the Product and Quotient Rules for $\sim$, we obtain

$$\dfrac{(8n)!}{((2n)!)^4} \sim \dfrac{\sqrt{16\pi n}\,(8n/e)^{8n}}{\left(\sqrt{4\pi n}\,(2n/e)^{2n}\right)^4}$$

$$= \dfrac{\sqrt{16\pi n}\,4^{8n}}{(\sqrt{4\pi n})^4} = \dfrac{1}{\pi^{3/2}}\,\dfrac{4^{8n-1}}{n^{3/2}}.$$

Hence

$$\lambda = 1/\pi^{3/2}.$$

4.8 By Stirling's Formula, and the Product and Quotient Rules for $\sim$, we obtain

$$\binom{3n}{n} = \dfrac{(3n)!}{n!\,(2n)!}$$

$$\sim \dfrac{\sqrt{6\pi n}\,(3n/e)^{3n}}{\sqrt{2\pi n}\,(n/e)^n\,\sqrt{4\pi n}\,(2n/e)^{2n}}$$

$$= \dfrac{\sqrt{3}}{\sqrt{4\pi n}}\,\dfrac{(3n)^{3n}}{n^n(2n)^{2n}}$$

$$= \sqrt{\dfrac{3}{4\pi n}}\,\dfrac{3^{3n}}{2^{2n}},$$

as required.

Standard primitives

$f(x)$	Primitive $F(x)$	Domain
$x^n,\ n \in \mathbb{Z} - \{-1\}$	$x^{n+1}/(n+1)$	$\mathbb{R}$ or $\mathbb{R} - \{0\}$
$x^\alpha,\ \alpha \neq -1$	$x^{\alpha+1}/(\alpha+1)$	$\mathbb{R}^+$
$a^x,\ a > 0$	$a^x/\log_e a$	$\mathbb{R}$
$\sin x$	$-\cos x$	$\mathbb{R}$
$\cos x$	$\sin x$	$\mathbb{R}$
$\tan x$	$\log_e(\sec x)$	$(-\tfrac{1}{2}\pi, \tfrac{1}{2}\pi)$
e^x	e^x	$\mathbb{R}$
$1/x$	$\log_e x$	$(0, \infty)$
$1/x$	$\log_e |x|$	$(-\infty, 0)$
$\log_e x$	$x\log_e x - x$	$(0, \infty)$
$\sinh x$	$\cosh x$	$\mathbb{R}$
$\cosh x$	$\sinh x$	$\mathbb{R}$
$\tanh x$	$\log_e(\cosh x)$	$\mathbb{R}$
$(a^2 - x^2)^{-1},\ a \neq 0$	$\dfrac{1}{2a}\log_e\left(\dfrac{a+x}{a-x}\right)$	$(-a, a)$
$(a^2 + x^2)^{-1},\ a \neq 0$	$\dfrac{1}{a}\tan^{-1}(x/a)$	$\mathbb{R}$
$(a^2 - x^2)^{-1/2},\ a \neq 0$	$\begin{cases} \sin^{-1}(x/a) \\ -\cos^{-1}(x/a) \end{cases}$	$\begin{matrix} (-a, a) \\ (-a, a) \end{matrix}$
$(x^2 - a^2)^{-1/2},\ a \neq 0$	$\begin{cases} \log_e(x + (x^2 - a^2)^{1/2}) \\ \cosh^{-1}(x/a) \end{cases}$	$\begin{matrix} (a, \infty) \\ (a, \infty) \end{matrix}$
$(a^2 + x^2)^{-1/2},\ a \neq 0$	$\begin{cases} \log_e(x + (a^2 + x^2)^{1/2}) \\ \sinh^{-1}(x/a) \end{cases}$	$\begin{matrix} \mathbb{R} \\ \mathbb{R} \end{matrix}$
$(a^2 - x^2)^{1/2},\ a \neq 0$	$\tfrac{1}{2}x(a^2 - x^2)^{1/2} + \tfrac{1}{2}a^2\sin^{-1}(x/a)$	$(-a, a)$
$(x^2 - a^2)^{1/2},\ a \neq 0$	$\tfrac{1}{2}x(x^2 - a^2)^{1/2} - \tfrac{1}{2}a^2\log_e(x + (x^2 - a^2)^{1/2})$	(a, ∞)
$(a^2 + x^2)^{1/2},\ a \neq 0$	$\tfrac{1}{2}x(a^2 + x^2)^{1/2} + \tfrac{1}{2}a^2\log_e(x + (a^2 + x^2)^{1/2})$	$\mathbb{R}$
$e^{ax}\cos bx,\ a, b \neq 0$	$\dfrac{e^{ax}}{a^2 + b^2}(a\cos bx + b\sin bx)$	$\mathbb{R}$
$e^{ax}\sin bx,\ a, b \neq 0$	$\dfrac{e^{ax}}{a^2 + b^2}(a\sin bx - b\cos bx)$	$\mathbb{R}$

Index